GR 12 18 69

The Slide Rule
AND ITS USE IN
Problem Solving

Second Edition

George C. Beakley

Arizona State University

H. W. Leach

Bell Helicopter Company

The Macmillan Company   **Collier-Macmillan Limited / London**

Preface

Material in this book has been prepared for students who wish to obtain facility in using the slide rule and solving technical problems. The subject matter is arranged so that it is suitable both for classroom use and for individual study. In presenting the text material, the authors have stressed the practical application of mathematical tools to help the student grasp the role of mathematical skills in problem solving situations.

The section on the slide rule has been arranged so that the student can follow the examples shown for each operation using the rule and then can practice and check his progress with a set of problems for which answers are given. This material will also be an excellent manual on use of the slide rule in future years.

The section on problem solving is designed to present situations involving the application of basic physical principles. The student is encouraged not only to use step-by-step reasoning in analyzing each problem but also to present the solution in a neat and orderly manner.

Answers for selected problems are given in the Appendix. The Appendix also includes frequently used constants, tables, and formulas.

The authors wish to express appreciation to the many professors, students, and engineers in industry who have contributed suggestions for material covered in this book. Their comments have been very helpful in the selection and presentation of the subject matter. Special appreciation is expressed to Donald Robbins and Leigh Hendricks of the Sandia Corporation, Albuquerque, New Mexico, who have provided the electronic computer produced design that has been reproduced on the cover of the text.

The authors are especially interested in learning the opinions of those who read this book concerning its utility and serviceability in meeting the needs for which it was written. Improvements that are suggested will be considered for incorporation in later editions.

G. C. B.

H. W. L.

Contents

Contents

vi

APPENDIXES

Part One

The Slide Rule

The slide rule is not a modern invention although its extensive use in business and industry has been common only in recent years. Since the slide rule is a mechanical device whereby the logarithms of numbers may be manipulated, the slide rule of today was made possible over three and a half centuries ago with the invention of logarithms by John Napier, Baron of Merchiston in Scotland. Although Napier did not publicly announce his system of logarithms until 1614, he had privately communicated a summary of his results to Tycho Brahe, a Danish astronomer in 1594. Napier set forth his purpose with these words:

> Seeing there is nothing (right well beloved Students of Mathematics) that is so troublesome to mathematical practice, nor doth more molest and hinder calculators, than the multiplications, divisions, square and cubical extractions of great numbers, which besides the tedious expense of time are for the most part subject to many slippery errors, I began therefore to consider in my mind by what certain and ready art I might remove those hindrances.

In 1620 Edmund Gunter, Professor of Astronomy at Gresham College, in London, conceived the idea of using logarithm scales that were constructed with antilogarithm markings for use in simple mathematical operations. William Oughtred, who lived near London, first used "Gunter's logarithm scales" in 1630 in sliding combination, thereby creating the first slide rule. Later he also placed the logarithm scales in circular form for use as a "circular slide rule."

Sir Isaac Newton, John Warner, John Robertson, Peter Roget, and Lieutenant Amédée Mannheim further developed these logarithmic scales until there exist today many types and shapes of rules. Basically all rules of modern manufacture are variations of a general type of construction that utilizes sliding scales and a movable indicator. The principles of operation are the same and they are not difficult to master.

DESCRIPTION OF THE SLIDE RULE

The slide rule consists of three main parts, the "body," the "slide," and the "indicator" (see Figure 10–1). The "body" of the rule is fixed; the "slide" is the middle sliding portion; and the "indicator," which may slide right or left on the body of the rule, is the transparent runner. A finely etched line on each side of the indicator is used to improve the accuracy in making settings and for locating the answer. This line is referred to as the "hairline."

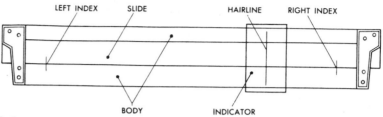

Figure 10–1.

The mark opposite the primary number 1 on the C and D scale is referred to as the "index" of the scale. An examination of the C and D scales indicates that each scale has two indexes: one at the left end (called the "left index") and one at the right end (called the "right index").

Regardless of the manufacturer or the specific model of slide rule that may be used, the principles of operation are the same. The nomenclature used here is general although some specific references are made to the Deci-Lon (Keuffel & Esser Co.), the Versalog (Frederick Post Co.), the Maniphase Multiplex (Eugene Dietzgen Co.), and the Model 800 ES (Pickett & Eckel, Inc.) rules. These models are those most frequently used by engineers, scientists, and technicians.

CARE OF THE SLIDE RULE

The slide rule is a precision instrument and should be afforded reasonable care in order to preserve its accuracy. Modern rules stand up well under normal usage, but dropping the rule or striking objects with it will probably impair its accuracy.

In use, the rule may collect dirt under the glass of the indicator. Inserting a piece of paper under the glass and sliding the indicator across it will frequently dislodge the dirt without necessitating the removal of the indicator glass from the frame. If the glass has to be removed for cleaning, it should be realigned when replaced, using the techniques described below.

The rule should never be washed with abrasive materials, alcohol, or other solvents, since these may remove markings. If the rule needs to be cleaned, it may be wiped carefully with a damp cloth, but the excessive use of water should be avoided because it will cause wooden rules to warp.

The metal-frame rules are not subject to warping due to moisture changes, but they must be protected against blows which would bend them or otherwise throw them out of alignment. A light layer of lubricant of the type specified by the manufacturer of the metal rule will increase the ease with which the working parts move. This is particularly important during the "breaking in" period of the new rule.

MANIPULATION OF THE RULE

Some techniques in manipulation of the rule have been found to speed up the setting of the slide and indicator. Two of these suggested procedures are described in the following paragraphs.

1. Settings usually can be made more rapidly by using two hands and holding the rule so that the thumbs are on the bottom with the backs of the hands toward the operator.

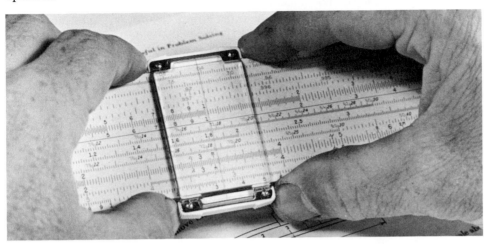

Illustration 10–1. In setting the indicator, a rolling motion with the forefingers will permit rapid and precise locations to be made. Keeping the fingers of both hands in contact with the indicator, exert slight forces toward each other with both hands.

2. In moving either the indicator or the slide, the settings are easier to make if the index fingers and thumbs of both hands are used to apply forces toward each other than if only one hand is used to apply force. For example, in setting the indicator, put the forefinger of each hand against the respective edges of the indicator and move it by a combined squeezing and rolling motion of the forefingers. The same general procedure is used in setting the slide, where both hands exert forces toward each other. The student is cautioned in setting the slide not to squeeze the frame of the rule, since this will cause the slide to bind.

Illustration 10–2. In moving the slide, use fingers to exert forces toward each other. A rolling motion with the forefinger aids in setting the indexes. Avoid pinching the frame because this will make the slide bind.

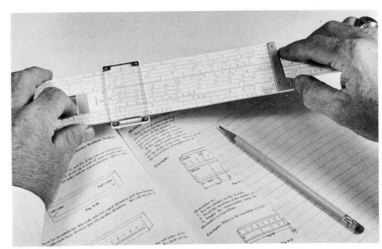

ADJUSTING THE RULE

Regardless of the make, most rules have the same general form of adjustment. The method of adjustment is simple but should not be applied in a hurry. It is desirable to use a magnifying glass, if one if available, to aid in lining up the scales and hairline.

To determine whether or not a rule needs adjustment, line up the indexes of the C and D scales. The indexes of the scales above and below the C and D scales should also be aligned. If they do not coincide, slightly loosen the screws that clamp the top bar of the frame and carefully move the frame to the right or left until the indexes are aligned. Tighten the screws slightly and move the slide to check for proper friction. If the alignment and friction are satisfactory, tighten the frame screws to complete that part of the adjustment.

Next, test the hairline for proper alignment by setting the hairline over the indexes of the C and D scales and checking to see that the hairline also coincides with the other indexes on this side of the rule. If it does not coincide with all the scale indexes, slightly loosen the screws which hold the glass frame to the indicator. Rotate the frame slowly until the hairline coincides with the indexes on this side of the rule. Tighten the screws holding this frame; then, while the hairline is aligned on the indexes of the C and D scales, turn the rule over and check for the alignment of the hairline with the indexes of the scales on the other side of the rule. If the hairline does not coincide with the indexes on this side of the rule, loosen the screws on the indicator and make the necessary adjustment as before.

Check the tightness of all screws when the adjustment is completed. The student is cautioned not to use excessive force in tightening any screws, as the threads may become stripped. With reasonable care, a slide rule will usually require very little adjustment over a considerable period of time.

ACCURACY OF THE RULE

Most measurements made in scientific work contain from two to four significant figures; that is, digits which are considered to be reliable. Since the mathematical operations of multiplication, division, and processes involving roots and powers will not increase the number of significant figures when the answer is obtained, the slide rule maintains an accuracy of three or four significant figures. The reliability of the digits obtained from the rule depends upon the precision with which the operator makes his settings. It is generally assumed that with a 10-in. slide rule, the error of the answer will not exceed about a tenth of 1 per cent. This is one part in a thousand.

A common tendency is to use more than three or four significant digits in such numbers as π (3.14159265 $\cdots$) and ϵ (2.71828 $\cdots$). The slide rule automatically "rounds off" such numbers to three or four significant figures thus preventing false accuracy (such as can occur in longhand operations) from occurring in the answer.

In slide rule calculations the answer should be read to four significant figures if the first digit in the answer is 1 (10.62, 1.009, 1195., 1,833,000., etc.). In other cases the answer is usually read to three significant figures (2.95, 872., 54,600., etc.). The chance for error is increased as the number of operations in a problem increases. However, for average length operations, such as those required to solve the problems in this text, the fourth significant digit in the slide rule answer should not vary more than ±2 from the correct answer. Where only three significant digits are read from the rule, the third digit should be within ±2 of the correct answer.

Example:

$$+ \left.\begin{array}{c} 16.27 \\ 16.26 \end{array}\right\} \text{within slide rule accuracy} \left\{\begin{array}{c} 0.0859 \\ 0.0858 \end{array}\right. +$$

| Correct Answer   16.25 | | 0.0857   Correct Answer |

$$- \left.\begin{array}{c} 16.24 \\ 16.23 \end{array}\right\} \text{within slide rule accuracy} \left\{\begin{array}{c} 0.0856 \\ 0.0855 \end{array}\right. -$$

Rules of modern manufacture are designed so that results read from the graduations are as reliable as the naked eye can distinguish. The use of magnifying devices may make the settings easier to locate but usually do not have an appreciable effect on the accuracy of the result.

INSTRUCTIONS FOR READING SCALE GRADUATIONS

Before studying the scales of the slide rule, let us review the reading of scale graduations in general. First let us examine a common 12-in. ruler (Figure 10–2).

Figure 10–2.

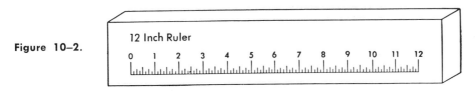

Example: We see that the total length of 1 ft has been divided into twelve equal parts and that each part is further divided into quarters, eighths, and sixteenths. This subdivision is necessary so that the workman need not estimate fractional parts of an inch.

Example: Measure the unknown lengths L_1 and L_2 as shown in Figure 10–3.

Figure 10–3.

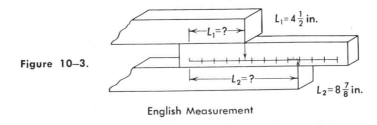

English Measurement

The English system of measurement as shown in Figure 10–3 is probably familiar to all students. The unit of length in the metric system which corresponds to the yard in the English system is called the *meter*. The meter is 39.37 in. in length.

For convenience, the meter is divided into one hundred equal parts called *centi-meters,* and each centimeter is divided into ten equal parts called *millimeters.* Since we can express units and fractional parts of units as tenths or hundredths of the length of a unit, this system of measurement is preferred many times for engineering work.

Example: Measure the unknown lengths L_1 and L_2 as shown in Figure 10–4.

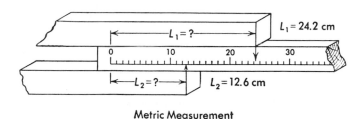

Metric Measurement

Figure 10–4.

The scales of the slide rule are basically divided as in the metric system in that between each division there are ten subdivisions. However, the student will find that the main divisions are not equal distances apart. Sometimes the divisions will be subdivided by graduations, and at other times the student will need to estimate the subdivisions by eye. Let us examine the D scale of a slide rule (Figure 10–5).

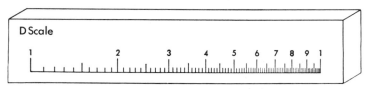

Figure 10–5.

Since the graduations are so close together, let us examine the rule in three portions: from left index to 2, from 2 to 4, and from 4 to the right index.

Example: Left index to 2 as shown in Figure 10–6.

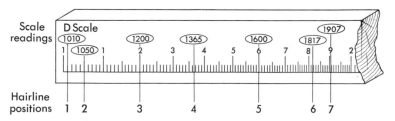

Figure 10–6.

The student should refer to his own rule for comparisons as he studies the diagrams in this chapter. In the example using Figure 10–6, we note that from the left index (read as one-zero-zero) to the digit 1 (read as one-one-zero), there are ten graduations. The first is read as *one-zero-one* (101), the second as *one-*

zero-two (102), etc. Digit 2 is read as *one-two-zero* (120), digit 3 as *one-three-zero* (130), etc. If need be, the student can subdivide by eye the distance between each of the small, unnumbered graduations. Thus, if the hairline is moved to position 4 (see example above), the reading would be *one-three-six five* or 1365. Position 6 might be read as 1817 and position 7 as 1907. The student is reminded that each small graduation on this portion of the rule has a value of 1.

Example: 2 to 4 as shown in Figure 10–7.

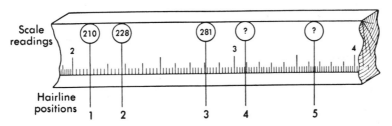

Figure 10–7.

Since the distance between 2 and 3 is not as long as the distance from the left index to 2, no numbers are placed over the graduations. However, we can use the same reasoning and subdivide as in the previous examples. Set the hairline in position 1 (see example) and read *two-one-zero,* or 210. We note that the distance between 200 and 210 has been divided into five divisions. Each subdivision would thus have a value of 2. Consequently, if the hairline is in position 2, a reading of 228 would be obtained. Remember that each of the smallest graduations is valued at 2 and not 1. What are the readings at 3, 4, and 5?[1]

Example: 4 to the right index as shown in Figure 10–8.

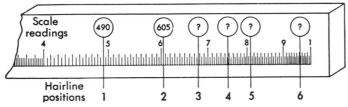

Figure 10–8.

The distance between 4 and 5 is still shorter than the distance between 3 and 4, and it becomes increasingly more difficult to print such small subdivisions. For this reason there are ten main divisions between 4 and 5, each of which is subdivided into two parts. With this type of marking it is possible to read two figures and estimate the third, or to get three significant figures on all readings. If the hairline is set as indicated in position 1, the reading would be *four-nine-zero* (490), and position 2 would give *six-zero-five* (605). What are the readings at hairline positions 3, 4, 5, and 6?[2]

[1] Readings at 3, 4, and 5 are respectively 281, 309, and 365.
[2] Readings at 3, 4, 5, and 6 are respectively 678, 746, 810, and 963.

Problems on Scale Readings

Read Answer on

SET HAIRLINE TO	ST SCALE	T SCALE	LL$_3$ SCALE	CI SCALE	K SCALE	DF SCALE	LL$_{01}$ SCALE	LL$_2$ SCALE	L SCALE
1. 210 on D									
2. 398 on D									
3. 1056 on D									
4. 1004 on D									
5. 866 on D									
6. 222 on D									
7. 1196 on D									
8. 439 on D									
9. 5775 on D									
10. 2325 on D									
11. 917 on D									
12. 323 on D									
13. 1077 on D									
14. 1854 on D									
15. 268 on D									
16. 833 on D									
17. 551 on D									
18. 667 on D									
19. 8125 on D									
20. 406 on D									
21. 918 on D									
22. 5775 on D									
23. 1466 on D									
24. 288 on D									
25. 466 on D									
26. 798 on D									
27. 1107 on D									
28. 396 on D									
29. 1999 on D									
30. 998 on D									

If the student has followed the reasoning thus far, he should have little trouble in determining how to read an indicated value on any scale of the slide rule. Several of the problems on page 8 should be worked, and the student should thoroughly understand the principle of graduation subdivision before he attempts to delve further into the uses of the slide rule.

It is suggested that one have a good understanding of logarithms before proceeding to learn the operational aspects of the slide rule. Those who may desire to review these principles should refer to Appendix I.

CONSTRUCTION OF THE SCALES

Let us examine how the main scales (C and D) of the rule are constructed. As a basis for this examination, let us set up a scale of some length with a beginning graduation called a *left index* and an end graduation called a *right index* as in Figure 10–9.

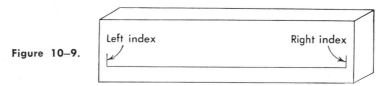

Figure 10–9.

Next let us subdivide this scale into ten equal divisions and then further subdivide each large division into ten smaller divisions as shown in Figure 10–10. We call this the *L scale*.

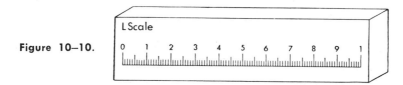

Figure 10–10.

Let us place a blank scale beneath this L scale so that the left index of the L scale will coincide with the left index of the blank scale as shown in Figure 10–11. We shall call the blank scale the *D scale*.

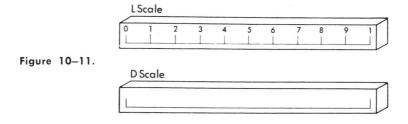

Figure 10–11.

Now let us graduate the D scale in such a way that each division mark is directly beneath the mark on the L scale that represents the mantissa of the logarithm of the number. Before examining the scales closer, we should note that the mantissa of 2 is 0.3010, the mantissa of 3 is 0.4771, the mantissa of 4 is 0.6021, and the mantissa of 5 is 0.6990 as shown in Figure 10–12.

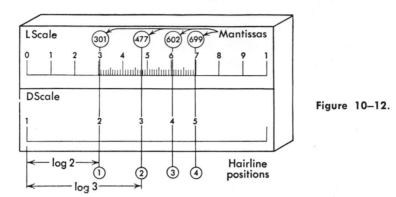

Figure 10–12.

If the student will examine his rule, he will find a C or D scale and an L scale. The C and D scales are identical, so use the D scale since it is printed on the body of the rule. Several problems should be worked, determining the logarithms of numbers by using the slide rule.

Remember to:

1. Set the number on the D scale.
2. Read the mantissa of the number on the L scale.
3. Supply the characteristic, using the *characteristic rules* given in the discussion on logarithms.

Example: What is the logarithm of 55.8? Use Figure 10–13.

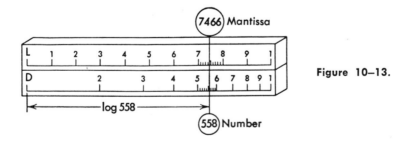

Figure 10–13.

From slide rule: Mantissa of 55.8 = 0.7466
From characteristic rules: Characteristic of 55.8 = 1.0000
Therefore   log of 55.8 = 1.7466

From the preceding example, we can see that the D scale is so constructed that each number lies below the mantissa of its logarithm. Also we note that the distance from the left index of the D scale to any number on the D scale represents (in length) the mantissa of the number as shown in Figure 10–14. Since the characteristic of a logarithm is governed merely by the location of the decimal point, we can delay its determination for the time being.

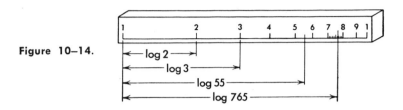

Figure 10–14.

Problems

10–1. Use the slide rule and find the logarithms.

a. 894.	*j.* 5.91×10^7	*s.* 33.67×10^{-9}
b. 1.845	*k.* 9.06×10^{-4}	*t.* 4.40×10^3
c. 0.438	*l.* 66.9×10^8	*u.* 98,700
d. 81.5	*m.* 155.8×10^2	*v.* 40.3×10^{-9}
e. 604.	*n.* 23.66×10^{-4}	*w.* 21.8×10^9
f. 7.41	*o.* 0.06641×10^8	*x.* 1.057×10^{-3}
g. 11.91	*p.* 9.33×10^{-2}	*y.* $719. \times 10^5$
h. 215.	*q.* 29.88×10^{-1}	*z.* 49.2×10^7
i. 993,000.	*r.* 0.552×10^6	

MULTIPLICATION

As shown in Figure 10–15, the C and D scales are divided logarithmically with all graduations being marked with their corresponding antilogarithms. These scales can be used for multiplication by adding a given logarithmic length on one of the scales to another logarithmic length which may be found on the other scale.

Example: $(2)(3) = 6$, as shown in Figure 10–15.

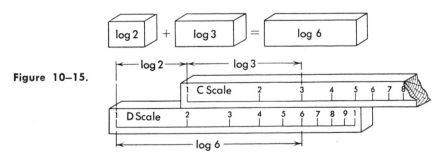

Figure 10–15.

PROCEDURE:

1. Set the left index of the C scale above the digit 2 on the D scale.
2. Move the hairline to the right until it is directly over 3 on the C scale.
3. Read the answer (6) directly under the hairline on the D scale.

The A and B scales are also divided logarithmically, but their overall lengths are only one half the lengths of the C and D scales. Therefore, although the A and B scales can also be used for multiplication and division, their shortened lengths will diminish the accuracy of the readings.

Similarly other pairs of scales of the slide rule may be used to perform multiplication if they are graduated logarithmically. A majority of slide rules have at least one set of folded scales that can be used for this purpose. Most frequently they are folded at π(3.14159 . . .). Special use of these scales will be explained later in this chapter.

In some cases when the logarithm of one number is added to the logarithm of another number, the multiplier extends out into space, and it is impossible to move the indicator to the product (Figure 10–16).

Example: (3)(4) = ?, as shown in Figure 10–16.

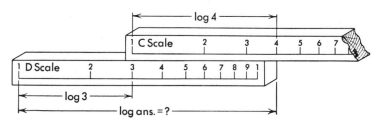

Figure 10–16.

In this case it is necessary to relocate the right index of the C scale above the figure 3 on the D scale and move the hairline to 4 on the C scale as shown in Figure 10–17.

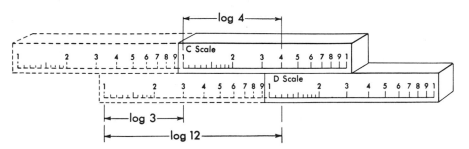

Figure 10–17.

PROCEDURE:

1. Set the right index of the C scale above the digit 3 on the D scale.
2. Move the hairline to the left until it is directly over 4 on the C scale.
3. Read answer (12) directly under the hairline on the D scale.

The location of the decimal point in multiplication problems is ascertained either by inspection or by applying one of the several methods explained in the following paragraphs.

METHODS OF DETERMINING DECIMAL POINT LOCATION

Several methods which may be used are given below. Although these methods by no means include all ways to determine the decimal point location, they will be suitable for instruction of students, particularly those having an elementary mathematical background.

Inspection Method

This is the simplest method and consists of determining the decimal point location by observing the location of the decimal point in the numbers involved in a slide rule operation and locating the decimal point in the answer by a quick estimation.

Example: $\dfrac{(28.1)}{(7.20)} = 390$ (decimal point to be determined)

A quick examination of the numbers involved shows that the answer will be somewhere near the number "4," so the answer evidently will be 3.90. This method will have its widest application where only one or two operations are involved and where the numbers lie between 1 and 100.

Example: $(1.22)(58.2) = 70.9$

In the example above, it is seen that the number 58.2 is multiplied by a number which is a little more than 1. Therefore, the answer will be slightly greater than 58.2.

Approximate Number Method

This method is an extension of the inspection method. It involves the same general procedures except that the numbers used in a problem are "rounded off" and written down and an approximate answer is obtained that will show the decimal point location.

Example: $(37.6)(0.188)(5.71)(11.92) = 482$ (decimal point to be located)

Rewrite, using simple numbers that are near in value to the problem numbers.

$$[(40)(0.2)][(6)(10)] = (8)(60) = 480$$

This shows that the answer in the example problem should be expressed as 482.

A problem that is more involved can be solved by this method, as shown by the following example.

Example: $\dfrac{(12,560)(0.0387)}{(594,000)} = 819$ (decimal point to be determined)

Using simple numbers near in value to the problem numbers, write the same problem:

$$\frac{(12,000)(0.04)}{(600,000)} = 0.0008$$

By cancellation the numbers can be simplified still further to obtain an approximate answer of 0.0008. One way of doing this would be to divide 12,000 into 600,000, obtaining a value of 50 in the denominator. This value of 50 divided into 0.04 gives 0.0008. Referring to the original problem, the decimal point must be located to give an answer of 0.000819.

Scientific Notation or Power-of-Ten Method

The power-of-ten or scientific notation method is a variation of the characteristic method discussed later in this book. In this method the numbers in the problem are expressed as a single digit, a decimal point, the remaining digits, and followed by the number "10" that is raised to the appropriate power. This process simplifies the numbers, and the decimal point in the answer can be determined by inspection or by the approximation method.

Example:

$$(15.9)\ (0.0077)\ (30500)\ (4660) = 1741 \text{ (decimal point to be located)}$$

The next step is to write the same problem with each number expressed as a digit, decimal point, and the remaining digits followed by the appropriate power of 10.

$$(1.59 \times 10^1)(7.7 \times 10^{-3})(3.05 \times 10^4)(4.66 \times 10^3) = 174.1 \times 10^5$$

Since all the numbers are now expressed as numbers between 1 and 10, followed by 10 to a power, the approximate value of the multiplication can be determined rapidly, by inspection, to be about 170. The power of 10 is obtained by adding algebraically the powers of 10 of each of the rewritten numbers. The answer to the original problem is therefore 174.1×10^5, or 17,410,000, or 1.741×10^7.

Example: $\dfrac{(28,500)\ (307)}{(0.552)} = 1585$ (decimal point to be located)

Rewrite the problem using powers of 10:

$$\frac{(2.85 \times 10^4)(3.07 \times 10^2)}{(5.52 \times 10^{-1})} = 1.585 \times 10^7$$

By inspection and approximation the product of the numerator will be found to be near 9, and dividing 5.52 into it will give about 1.6. This procedure determines the decimal point location for the digits of the answer. The powers of 10 are added algebraically to give 10^7, which completes the decimal point location in the answer. The answer may be rewritten as 15,850,000 if desired.

Digit Method

In this method the numbers of digits in each number are counted and the following rules apply.

Multiplication. Add the number of digits to the left of the decimal of each number to be multiplied. This will give the number of digits to the left of the decimal in the answer. If the slide projects to the right, subtract one from the number of digits to be pointed off.

Example: $(27,300)(15.1) = 412,000$

There are five digits to be counted in the first number and only two digits in the second number. Since the slide projects to the right, subtract 1. There will be six digits to the left of the decimal point in the answer.

Division. Subtract the number of digits to the left of the decimal in the denominator from the number of digits to the left of the decimal in the numerator to obtain the number of digits to the left of the decimal in the answer. If the slide projects to the right in division, add one digit more to be pointed off.

Example: $\dfrac{(12.88)}{(466)} = 0.0276$

Subtracting three digits in the denominator from two digits in the numerator gives (-1) digit to be located in the answer. Inspection shows that the answer will be a decimal quantity. In any case where decimal numbers are encountered, the method of counting the digits is to begin at the decimal point and count the number of zeroes between the decimal point and the first digit that is not zero to the right of the decimal. Since the digit difference shown above is (-1), there must be one zero between the decimal point and the first significant figure, which gives an answer of 0.0276. The student will observe that the digit count of decimal numbers is considered as a minus quantity and that the addition and subtraction of the digit count must take into account any minus signs.

Variations and extensions of these methods may readily be set up to solve problems involving roots and powers. Many schools prefer the "characteristic" or "projections method" to determine decimal point location, and this method is given in detail in the discussions which follow.

Characteristic Method

Projection Rule for Multiplication. This method of decimal point location is recommended for students who are inexperienced in slide rule computations:

1. Before attempting to solve the problem, place the characteristic of each quantity above or below it.

2. Solve for the sum of the characteristics by simple addition, and place this number above the space for the answer.

3. Begin the multiplication with the slide rule, and each time the left index of the C scale extends past the left index of the D scale, add a $(+1)$ to the sum of the characteristics previously determined.

4. Add the original sum to the $+1$'s obtained from left extensions. The total number is the characteristic of the answer.

Example:

one left extension
↓

CHARACTERISTICS. $(0) + (0) \to (0) + 1 = +1 \leftarrow$ characteristic of answer

(5) (3) = $\underline{\underline{15}}$ Answer

> ESTIMATION OF ANSWER BY SCIENTIFIC NOTATION:
> $(5)(3) = \underline{\underline{1.5(10)^1}} \leftarrow$ ESTIMATED ANSWER

Example:

one left extension
↓

CHARACTERISTICS. $(+2) + (-3) \to (-1) + 1 = 0$

(390) (0.0030) = $\underline{\underline{1.17}}$ Answer

> ESTIMATION OF ANSWER BY SCIENTIFIC NOTATION:
> $(4)(10)^2(3)(10)^{-3} = \underline{\underline{1.2(10)^0}} \leftarrow$ ESTIMATED ANSWER

Example:

two left
↓ extensions

CHARACTERISTICS. $(-3) + (+1) + (+2) + (+4) \to (+4) + 2 = +6$

(0.001633) (79.1) (144) (96,500) = $\underline{\underline{1,800,000}}$ Answer

> ESTIMATION OF ANSWER BY SCIENTIFIC NOTATION:
> $(2)(10)^{-3}(8)(10)^1(1)(10)^2(10)^5 = \underline{\underline{1.6(10)^6}} \leftarrow$ ESTIMATED ANSWER

Example:

three left
↓ extensions

CHARACTERISTICS.

$(+1) + (+3) + (-3) + (-4) \to (-3) + 3 = 0$

(73.7) (4460) (0.00704) (0.000853) = $\underline{\underline{1.975}}$ Answer

> ESTIMATION OF ANSWER BY SCIENTIFIC NOTATION:
> $(7)(10)^1(4)(10)^3(7)(10)^{-3}(9)(10)^{-4} = \underline{\underline{1.8(10)^0}} \leftarrow$ ESTIMATED ANSWER

Example:

two left extensions
↓

CHARACTERISTICS. $(+2) + (+2) + (0) \to (+4) + \overbrace{1+1}^{} = +6$

(861) (204) (9.0) = 1,580,000 or $\underline{\underline{(1.58)(10)^6}}$ Answer

> ESTIMATION OF ANSWER BY SCIENTIFIC NOTATION:
> $(9)(10)^2(2)(10)^2(9) = \underline{\underline{1.6(10)^6}} \leftarrow$ ESTIMATED ANSWER

Multiplication Practice Problems

10–2. $(23.8)(31.6) = (7.52)(10)^2$
10–3. $(105.6)(4.09) = (4.32)(10)^2$
10–4. $(286,000)(0.311) = (8.89)(10)^4$
10–5. $(0.0886)(196.2) = (1.738)(10)^1$
10–6. $(0.769)(47.2) = (3.63)(10)^1$
10–7. $(60.7)(17.44) = (1.059)(10)^3$
10–8. $(9.16)(115.7) = (1.060)(10)^3$
10–9. $(592.)(80.1) = (4.74)(10)^4$
10–10. $(7.69 \times 10^3)(0.722 \times 10^{-6}) = (5.55)(10)^{-3}$
10–11. $(37.5 \times 10^{-1})(0.0974 \times 10^{-3}) = (3.65)(10)^{-4}$
10–12. $(23.9)(0.715)(106.2) = (1.815)(10)^3$
10–13. $(60.7)(1059)(237,000) = (1.523)(10)^{10}$
10–14. $(988)(8180)(0.206) = (1.665)(10)^6$
10–15. $(11.14)(0.0556)(76.3 \times 10^{-6}) = (4.73)(10)^{-5}$
10–16. $(72.1)(\pi)(66.1) = (1.497)(10)^4$
10–17. $(0.0519)(16.21)(1.085) = (9.13)(10)^{-1}$
10–18. $(0.001093)(27.6)(56,700) = (1.710)(10)^3$
10–19. $(0.379)(0.00507)(0.414) = (7.96)(10)^{-4}$
10–20. $(16.05)(23.9)(0.821) = (3.15)(10)^2$
10–21. $(1009)(0.226)(774) = (1.765)(10)^5$
10–22. $(316)(825)(67,600) = (1.762)(10)^{10}$
10–23. $(21,000)(0.822)(16.92) = (2.92)(10)^5$
10–24. $(0.707)(80.6)(0.451) = (2.57)(10)^1$
10–25. $(1.555 \times 10^3)(27.9 \times 10^5)(0.902 \times 10^{-7}) = (3.91)(10)^2$
10–26. $(0.729)(10)^3(22,500)(33.2) = (5.45)(10)^8$
10–27. $(18.97)(0.216)(899)(\pi)(91.2) = (1.055)(10)^6$
10–28. $(7160)(0.000333)(26)(19.6)(5.01) = (6.09)(10)^3$
10–29. $(1.712)(89,400)(19.5)(10^{-5})(82.1) = (2.45)(10)^3$
10–30. $(62.7)(0.537)(0.1137)(0.806)(15.09) = (4.66)(10)^1$
10–31. $(10)^6(159.2)(144)(7,920,000)(\pi) = (5.70)(10)^{17}$
10–32. $(0.0771)(19.66)(219)(0.993)(7.05) = (2.32)(10)^3$
10–33. $(15.06)(\pi)(625)(0.0963)(43.4) = (1.236)(10)^5$
10–34. $(2160)(1802)(\pi)(292)(0.0443) = (1.582)(10)^8$
10–35. $(437)(1.075)(0.881)(43,300)(17.22) = (3.09)(10)^8$
10–36. $(\pi)(91.6)(555)(0.673)(0.00315)(27.7) = (9.38)(10)^3$
10–37. $(18.01)(22.3)(1.066)(19.36)(10)^{-5} = (8.29)(10)^{-2}$
10–38. $(84.2)(15.62)(921)(0.662)(0.1509) = (1.210)(10)^5$
10–39. $(66,000)(25.9)(10.62)(28.4)(77.6) = (4.00)(10)^{10}$
10–40. $(55.1)(7.33 \times 10^{-8})(76.3)(10)^5(0.00905) = (2.79)(10)^{-1}$
10–41. $(18.91)(0.257)(0.0811)(92,500)(\pi) = (1.145)(10)^5$

Multiplication Problems

10–42. $(46.8)(11.97)$
10–43. $(479.)(11.07)$
10–44. $(9.35)(77.8)$
10–45. $(10.09)(843,000.)$

10–46. $(77,900)(0.467)$
10–47. $(123.9)(0.00556)$
10–48. $(214.9)(66.06)$
10–49. $(112.2)(0.953)$

Multiplication Problems (continued)

10–50. $(87.0)(1.006)$
10–51. $(1,097,000)(1.984)$
10–52. $(43.8)(0.000779)$
10–53. $(31.05)(134.9)$
10–54. $(117.9)(98.9)$
10–55. $(55.6)(68.1)$
10–56. $(1.055)(85.3)$
10–57. $(33,050.)(16,900.)$
10–58. $(6.089)(44.87)$
10–59. $(34.8)(89.7)$
10–60. $(43,900.)(19.07)$
10–61. $(41.3)(87.9)$
10–62. $(99.7)(434,000.)$
10–63. $(0.0969)(0.1034)(0.1111)(0.1066)$
10–64. $(1.084 \times 10^{-5})(0.1758 \times 10^{13})(66.4)(0.901)$
10–65. $(234.5)(10)^4(21.21)(0.874)(0.0100)$
10–66. $(\pi)(26.88)(0.1682)(0.1463)(45.2)(1.007)$
10–67. $(75.8)(0.1044 \times 10^8)(10)^{-2}(54,000)(0.769)$
10–68. $(34.5)(31.09)(10)^{-6}(54.7)(0.677)(0.1003)$
10–69. $(6.08)(5.77)(46.8)(89.9)(3.02)(0.443)(\pi)$
10–70. $(1.055)(6.91)(31.9)(11.21)(\pi)(35.9)(4.09)$
10–71. $(10.68)(21.87)$
10–72. $(88,900.)(54.7)$
10–73. $(113,900.)(48.1)$
10–74. $(95,500.)(0.000479)$
10–75. $(0.0956)(147.2)(0.0778)$
10–76. $(15.47)(82.5)(975,000.)$
10–77. $(37.8)(22,490,000.)(0.15)$
10–78. $(1.048)(0.753)(0.933)$
10–79. $(1.856)(10)^3(21.98)$
10–80. $(57.7)(46.8)(3.08)$
10–81. $(0.045)(0.512)(115.4)$
10–82. $(0.307)(46.3)(7.94)$
10–83. $(2.229)(86.05)(16,090.)(\pi)$
10–84. $(44,090.)(38.9)(667.)(55.9)$
10–85. $(568.)(46.07)(3.41)(67.9)$
10–86. $(75.88)(0.0743)(0.1185)(0.429)$
10–87. $(10)^{-7}(69.8)(11.03)(0.901)$
10–88. $(46.3)(0.865)(10)^{-9}(0.953)(\pi)$
10–89. $(665.)(35,090)(0.1196)(0.469)$
10–90. $(888.)(35.9)(77.9)(0.652)$
10–91. $(43.4)(0.898)(70.09)(0.113)(\pi)$

DIVISION

Multiplication is merely the process of mechanically adding the logarithms of the quantities involved. From a review of the principles of logarithms, it follows that division is merely the process of mechanically subtracting the logarithm of the divisor from the logarithm of the dividend.

Example: $\dfrac{(8)}{(2)} = 4$

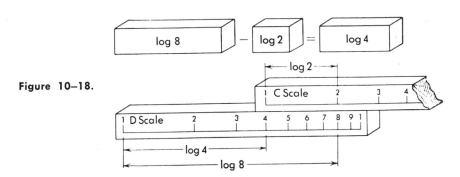

Figure 10–18.

PROCEDURE

1. Set the divisor (2) on the C scale directly above the dividend (8), which is located on the D scale.

2. Read the answer (4) on the D scale directly under the left index of the C scale.

For location of the decimal point in division problems the following *Projection Rule* should be observed.

Projection Rule for Division

1. Locate the characteristic of the dividend above it and the characteristic of the divisor below it.

2. Subtract the characteristic of the divisor from the characteristic of the dividend.

3. For every left extension of the C scale's left index, add a (-1) to the total characteristic already obtained.

4. The sum is the characteristic of the answer.

Example:

$$\underset{\text{(0)}}{\overset{(+2)}{\frac{(575)}{(6.05)}}} = \underset{\text{characteristic of answer}}{\overset{\text{left extension}}{(+2) - (0) \rightarrow +2 - 1 = +1}}$$

$$\frac{(575)}{(6.05)} = (9.50)(10)^1$$

ESTIMATION OF ANSWER BY SCIENTIFIC NOTATION:

$$\frac{6(10)^2}{6} = 1(10)^2 \leftarrow \text{ESTIMATED ANSWER}$$

Example:

left extension
characteristic of answer

$$\frac{\overset{(-1)}{(0.465)}}{\underset{(+1)}{(54)}} = (8.61)(10)^{-3} \qquad (-1) - (+1) \to -2 - \overset{\downarrow}{1} = \overset{\downarrow}{-3}$$

ESTIMATION OF ANSWER BY SCIENTIFIC NOTATION:

$$\frac{5(10)^{-1}}{5(10)^1} = 1(10)^{-2} \leftarrow \text{ESTIMATED ANSWER}$$

Division Practice Problems

10–92. $(29.6) \div (18.02) = 1.641$

10–93. $(1.532) \div (72.6) = (2.11)(10)^{-2}$

10–94. $(0.1153) \div (70.3) = (1.64)(10)^{-3}$

10–95. $(89.3) \div (115.6) = (7.72)(10)^{-1}$

10–96. $(0.1052) \div (33.6) = (3.13)(10)^{-3}$

10–97. $(40.2) \div (50.8) = (7.91)(10)^{-1}$

10–98. $(0.661) \div (70,500) = (9.38)(10)^{-6}$

10–99. $(182.9) \div (0.00552) = (3.31)(10)^4$

10–100. $(0.714) \div (98,200) = (7.27)(10)^{-6}$

10–101. $(4.36) \div (80,300) = (5.43)(10)^{-5}$

10–102. $(1.339) \div (22.6 \times 10^4) = (5.92)(10)^{-6}$

10–103. $(17.03) \div (76.3) = (2.23)(10)^{-1}$

10–104. $(0.511) \div (0.281) = 1.819$

10–105. $(67.7) \div (91,300) = (7.42)(10)^{-4}$

10–106. $(5.04) \div (29,800) = (1.691)(10)^{-4}$

10–107. $(18.35) \div (0.921) = (1.992)(10)^1$

10–108. $(29.6 \times 10^5) \div (0.905) = (3.27)(10)^6$

10–109. $(0.1037) \div (92.5 \times 10^5) = (1.121)(10)^{-8}$

10–110. $(537) \div (15.63 \times 10^{-7}) = (3.44)(10)^8$

10–111. $(26,300) \div (84.3 \times 10^5) = (3.12)(10)^{-3}$

10–112. $(6,370) \div (0.733) = (8.69)(10)^3$

10–113. $(1.066) \div (7.51 \times 10^3) = (1.419)(10)^{-4}$

10–114. $(29.6 \times 10^4) \div (0.973) = (3.04)(10)^5$

10–115. $(0.912) \div (10.31 \times 10^{-5}) = (8.85)(10)^3$

10–116. $(17.37 \times 10^{-4}) \div (0.662) = (2.62)(10)^{-3}$

10–117. $(0.693 \times 10^5) \div (1.008 \times 10^{-6}) = (6.88)(10)^{10}$

10–118. $(89.1) \times 10^3) \div (189.3 \times 10^4) = (4.71)(10)^{-2}$

10–119. $(0.617) \div (29,600) = (2.08)(10)^{-5}$

10–120. $(18.06 \times 10^7) \div (15.29) = (1.181)(10)^7$

10–121. $(56.8)(10)^4 \div (29.6)(10)^{-3} = (1.919)(10)^7$

10–122. $(183,600) \div (76.3 \times 10^{-3}) = (2.41)(10)^6$

10–123. $(75.9) \div (0.000813) = (9.34)(10)^4$

10–124. $(43.6) \div (0.0837) = (5.21)(10)^2$
10–125. $(156.8 \times 10^3) \div (0.715) = (2.19)(10)^5$
10–126. $(216 \times 10^{-3}) \div (1557) = (1.387)(10)^{-4}$
10–127. $(88.3 \times 10^{-1}) \div (29.1 \times 10^{-4}) = (3.03)(10)^3$
10–128. $(1.034 \times 10^3) \div (0.706 \times 10^{-8}) = (1.465)(10)^{11}$
10–129. $(55.2)(10)^3 \div (0.1556 \times 10^3) = (3.55)(10)^2$
10–130. $(0.01339) \div (1896 \times 10^5) = (7.06)(10)^{-11}$
10–131. $(4,030 \times 10^{-7}) \div (75.3 \times 10^{-9}) = (5.35)(10)^3$

Problems in Division

10–132. $\dfrac{89.9}{45.}$

10–133. $\dfrac{147.}{22.}$

10–134. $\dfrac{9.06}{7.1}$

10–135. $\dfrac{1,985.}{78.55}$

10–136. $\dfrac{19,230.}{64.88}$

10–137. $\dfrac{87,600.}{43.8}$

10–138. $\dfrac{54.8}{9.10}$

10–139. $\dfrac{0.877}{33.07}$

10–140. $\dfrac{11.44}{24.9}$

10–141. $\dfrac{187,900.}{71.45}$

10–142. $\dfrac{0.00882}{87.04}$

10–143. $\dfrac{0.675}{54.8}$

10–144. $\dfrac{87.9}{45.7}$

10–145. $\dfrac{164,800.}{3.88}$

10–146. $\dfrac{7.09 \times 10^3}{18.45}$

10–147. $\dfrac{(0.001755)}{(6.175)}$

10–148. $\dfrac{(0.0000559)}{(0.00659)}$

10–149. $\dfrac{(5.065)}{(0.0003375)}$

10–150. $\dfrac{(469,000)}{(793)}$

10–151. $\dfrac{(5,100,000)}{(933 \times 10^5)}$

10–152. $\dfrac{(3765 \times .10^3)}{(760.3)}$

10–153. $\dfrac{(4917)}{(0.391)}$

10–154. $\dfrac{(5516)}{(1.65)}$

10–155. $\dfrac{(0.0916)}{(0.331)}$

10–156. $\dfrac{(193.7)}{(5.06)}$

10–157. $\dfrac{(113.05)}{(72.35)}$

10–158. $\dfrac{(32.33)}{(46.77)}$

10–159. $\dfrac{(3.17)}{(3.1416)}$

10–160. $\dfrac{(0.221)}{(56.91)}$

10–161. $\dfrac{(233.17)}{(5506)}$

10–162. $\dfrac{(72.13)}{(52.03)}$

10–163. $\dfrac{(6607)}{(1.91 \times 10^5)}$

10–164. $\dfrac{(1.993 \times 10^{-8})}{(72.31 \times 10^{-6})}$

10–165. $\dfrac{(461 \times 10^3)}{(0.003617)}$

10–166. $\dfrac{(9903 \times 10^{-5})}{(47.31 \times 10^3)}$

10–167. $\dfrac{0.711}{11,980.}$

10–168. $\dfrac{0.01253}{66.8}$

10–169. $\dfrac{0.974}{1.058}$

10–170. $\dfrac{0.000497}{38.9 \times 10^{-5}}$

10–171. $\dfrac{48.6 \times 10^{-9}}{1.977 \times 10^5}$

10–172. $\dfrac{69,990. \times 10^{18}}{43.9 \times 10^{-2}}$

10–173. $\dfrac{5.06 \times 10^{-7}}{0.001853 \times 10^9}$

10–174. $\dfrac{1.097 \times 10^{-6}}{458. \times 10^{-1}}$

10–175. $\dfrac{89.99 \times 10^{-3}}{40.7 \times 10^{-6}}$

10–176. $\dfrac{659,000}{0.1148 \times 10^{-3}}$

10–177. $\dfrac{883.8}{3.89 \times 10^{-11}}$

10–178. $\dfrac{15.06 \times 10^{-7}}{33.8 \times 10^{-1}}$

10–179. $\dfrac{1.095}{24.66}$

10–180. $\dfrac{33.97 \times 10^7}{56.98 \times 10^3}$

10–181. $\dfrac{22,900. \times 10^{-6}}{76.4 \times 10^4}$

Combined Multiplication and Division

Since most scientific calculations involve both multiplication and division, the student should master the technique of combined multiplication and division. The projection rules for both multiplication and division also apply in a combination problem.

Example:

$$\frac{\overset{(+2)}{(513)}\ \overset{(+4)}{(15,300)}}{\underset{+2}{(238)}} \quad (+6)\ -(+2) \to +4$$
$$= 32,900, \text{ or } 3.29 \times 10^4$$

> ESTIMATION OF ANSWER BY SCIENTIFIC NOTATION:
>
> $$\frac{5(10)^2\ (1.5)(10)^4}{(2.5)\ (10)^2} = 3(10)^4 \leftarrow \text{ESTIMATED ANSWER}$$

In order to work the problem above, first set 513 divided by 238 on the C and D scales. Now, instead of reading this answer, move the hairline to 15,300 on the C scale (thus multiplying this latter quantity by the quotient of the first setting).

The student should always alternate the division and multiplication settings and should not try to take readings as he progresses with the steps. Only the final result is desired and, since each reading of the rule further magnifies any error, the fewest readings possible should be allowed.

Example:

(left extension from the division) ↓

$$\frac{\overset{(+1)}{(4730)}\overset{(-4)}{(0.000391)}\overset{(+2)}{(693.5)}}{\underset{(-1)}{(0.312)}\underset{(+1)}{(55.1)}\underset{(+2)}{(773.1)}} \quad (-1)-(+2) \to -3-1 = -4$$
$$= 9.66 \times 10^{-4}$$

> ESTIMATION OF ANSWER BY SCIENTIFIC NOTATION:
>
> $$\frac{5(10)^1\ 4(10)^{-4}\ 7(10)^2}{3(10)^{-1}\ 6(10)^1\ 8(10)^2} = 1(10)^{-3} \leftarrow \text{ESTIMATED ANSWER}$$

Remember that when you want to divide, you move the slide, and when you want to multiply, you move the hairline.

A common error committed by many students is to multiply all the quantities in the dividend and all the quantities in the divisor and then divide these two results. This is a bad habit and such practice should not be followed. There are too many chances for mistakes, in addition to the method's being slower.

Combined Multiplication and Division Practice Problems

10–182. $\dfrac{(29.6)(18.01)}{(937)} = (5.69)(10)^{-1}$

10–183. $\dfrac{(625,000)(0.0337)}{(48.2)} = (4.37)(10)^{2}$

10–184. $\dfrac{(0.887)(1,109)}{(5.22)} = (1.884)(10)^{2}$

10–185. $\dfrac{(0.1058)(937,000)}{(0.218)} = (4.55)(10)^{5}$

10–186. $\dfrac{(43,800)(0.0661)}{87.2 \times 10^{5})} = (3.32)(10)^{-4}$

10–187. $\dfrac{(114.3)(0.567)}{(66,400)} = (9.76)(10)^{-4}$

10–188. $\dfrac{(76.5 \times 10^{4})}{(0.733)(49.7 \times 10^{-6})} = (2.10)(10)^{10}$

10–189. $\dfrac{(11.03)}{(20,100)(8.72 \times 10^{3})} = (6.29)(10)^{-8}$

10–190. $\dfrac{(0.226)}{(87.3 \times 10^{4})(0.717)} = (3.61)(10)^{-7}$

10–191. $\dfrac{(43.2)}{(9.09)(0.000652)} = (7.29)(10)^{3}$

10–192. $\dfrac{(94.9 \times 10^{-9})}{(33,800)(0.609)} = (4.61)(10)^{-12}$

10–193. $\dfrac{(737,000)}{(0.1556)(61.9 \times 10^{3})} = (7.65)(10)^{1}$

10–194. $\dfrac{(17.01)(0.0336)}{(52,600)(0.01061)} = (1.024)(10)^{-3}$

10–195. $\dfrac{(66.6)(0.937)}{(7.05 \times 10^{2})(184,300)} = (4.80)(10)^{-7}$

10–196. $\dfrac{(2.96)(1000)(62.1)}{(0.911)(432,000)} = (4.67)(10)^{-1}$

10–197. $\dfrac{(45.8)(10.33)}{(29,200)(0.702)} = (2.31)(10)^{-2}$

10–198. $\dfrac{(0.604)(9,270)}{(0.817 \times 10^{4})(1.372)} = (4.99)(10)^{-1}$

10–199. $\dfrac{(176,300)(42.8 \times 10^{3})}{(68.3)(15.01)} = (7.36)(10)^{6}$

10–200. $\dfrac{(39,200)(89.3 \times 10^{-7})}{(20.4 \times 10^{-6})(155.5)} = (1.104)(10)^{2}$

10–201. $\dfrac{(0.763 \times 10^{-4})(0.01004)}{(44.3)(7,150,000)} = (2.42)(10)^{-15}$

10–202. $\dfrac{(152,300)(88,100)}{(0.00339)(60.4)} = (6.55)(10)^{10}$

10–203. $\dfrac{(90,400)(2.05 \times 10^{6})}{(24.3 \times 10^{-2})(0.0227)} = (3.36)(10)^{13}$

Combined Multiplication and Division Practice Problems (continued)

10–204. $\dfrac{(14.36 \times 10^2)(0.907)}{(51.6 \times 10^2)(0.00001118)} = (2.26)(10)^4$

10–205. $\dfrac{(991,000)(60.3 \times 10^4)}{(23.3 \times 10^{-1})(0.1996)} = (1.285)(10)^{12}$

10–206. $\dfrac{(8.40)(10)^3(29.6 \times 10^{-5})}{(0.369)(10.02 \times 10^9)} = (6.72)(10)^{-10}$

10–207. $\dfrac{(54.9)(26.8)(0.331)}{(21.6)(11.03)(54.6)} = (3.74)(10)^{-2}$

10–208. $\dfrac{(17,630)(0.1775)(92.3)}{(0.433)(0.0061)(57.3)} = (1.908)(10)^6$

10–209. $\dfrac{(0.821)(0.221)(0.811)}{(0.0907)(10.72)(66,300)} = (2.28)(10)^{-6}$

10–210. $\dfrac{(0.00552)(89.6)(0.705)}{(19.52 \times 10^3)(18.03)(22.4)} = (4.42)(10)^{-8}$

10–211. $\dfrac{(30,600)(29.9)(0.00777)}{(485)(19.32)(62.6)} = (1.212)(10)^{-2}$

10–212. $\dfrac{(54.1)(0.393)(16,070)}{(49.3 \times 10^3)(11.21)(61.6)} = (1.00)(10)^{-2}$

10–213. $\dfrac{(44.2)(100.7)(62,400)}{(90.3)(75,100)(0.01066)} = (3.84)(10)^3$

10–214. $\dfrac{(78.4)(15.59)(0.01669)}{(33.6)(88,100)(0.432)} = (1.594)(10)^{-5}$

10–215. $\dfrac{(994,000)(21,300)(0.1761)}{(44.4)(71.2)(32.1 \times 10^4)} = 3.67$

10–216. $\dfrac{(16.21)(678,000)(56.6)}{(0.01073)(4,980)(30.3)} = (3.84)(10)^5$

10–217. $\dfrac{(61.3 \times 10^3)(0.1718)(0.893)}{(21.6)(0.902)(0.01155)} = (4.18)(10)^4$

10–218. $\dfrac{(20,900)(16.22 \times 10^4)(0.1061)}{(877)(20.1 \times 10^{-4})(5.03)} = (4.06)(10)^7$

10–219. $\dfrac{(999,000)(17.33)(0.1562)}{(0.802)(0.0443)(29.3 \times 10^{-1})} = (2.60)(10)^7$

10–220. $\dfrac{(16.21)(0.0339)(151.6)(0.211)}{(0.00361)(0.785)(93.2)(406)} = (1.640)(10)^{-1}$

10–221. $\dfrac{(84.3)(0.916)(0.1133)(21.3)}{(66.2)(0.407)(55.3)(462)} = (2.72)(10)^{-4}$

Problems

Solve by combined multiplication and division method:

10–222. $\dfrac{(0.916)}{(90.5)(13.06)}$

10–223. $\dfrac{(0.00908)}{(22.3)(33.2)}$

10–224. $\dfrac{(24.5)(43)}{(36)}$

10–225. $\dfrac{(82)(9.3)}{(56.5)}$

10–226. $\dfrac{(167)(842)}{(0.976)}$

10–227. $\dfrac{(5.72)(3690)}{(95.7)}$

10–228. $\dfrac{(925)(76.9)}{(37.6)}$

10–229. $\dfrac{(9.87)}{(1.76)(89)}$

10–230. $\dfrac{(85.4)}{(26.3)(213)}$

10–231. $\dfrac{(1525)}{(73.6)(0.007)}$

10–232. $\dfrac{(84,500)}{(126)(37.3)}$

10–233. $\dfrac{(76)(23.7)}{(13.5)(373)}$

10–234. $\dfrac{(6.23)(2.14)}{(0.00531)}$

10–235. $\dfrac{(21.3)(370)}{(10.9)(758)}$

10–236. $\dfrac{(0.00215)(2520)}{(7.57)(118)}$

10–237. $\dfrac{(755)(1.15)}{(51.4)(0.093)}$

10–238. $\dfrac{(916)(0.752)}{(5.16)}$

10–239. $\dfrac{(23.1)(1.506)}{(6.27)}$

10–240. $\dfrac{(42.6)(1.935)}{(750.3)}$

10–241. $\dfrac{(77.1)(10.53)}{(331.0)(73)}$

10–242. $\dfrac{(56.7)(0.00336)}{(15.06)(8.23)}$

10–243. $\dfrac{(14.5)(10)^3(6.22)}{(53.3)(0.00103)}$

10–244. $\dfrac{(42)(1000)}{(5.23)(0.00771)}$

10–245. $\dfrac{(1.331)}{(9.16)(506)}$

10–246. $\dfrac{(4320)(0.7854)}{(134)(0.9)}$

10–247. $\dfrac{(0.00713)(329)}{(0.0105)(1000)}$

10–248. $\dfrac{(103.4)(0.028)}{(0.0798)}$

10–249. $\dfrac{(1573)(4618)}{(3935)(97)}$

10–250. $\dfrac{(47.2)(0.0973)}{(85)(37.6)}$

10–251. $\dfrac{(0.0445)(0.0972)}{(0.218)(0.318)}$

10–252. $\dfrac{(39.1)(680,000)(3.52)(1.1 \times 10^6)}{(0.0316)(9.6 \times 10^6)(26.3)}$

10–253. $\dfrac{(7.69)(76,000)(5.63)(0.00314)}{(0.00365)(10 \times 10^6)}$

10–254. $\dfrac{(3.97)(6.71 \times 10^{-3})(0.067)}{(63.1)(3 \times 10^7)(7.61)(80,175)}$

10–255. $\dfrac{(697)(0.000713)(68.1)}{(234)(9.68)(5.1 \times 10^4)}$

10–256. $\dfrac{(43,400)(9.16)(8.1 \times 10^{-6})}{(0.00613)(67,000)(0.416)}$

10–257. $\dfrac{(691.6)(7.191)(3 \times 10^7)}{(410,000)(6.39)(0.0876)}$

10–258. $\dfrac{(37.615)(81.4)(9.687)(0.0017)}{(13.13)(0.076)(43)}$

10–259. $\dfrac{(51.2 \times 10^{-6})(3.41 \times 10^5)(36.1)}{(96.69)(7 \times 10^{-2})(0.134)}$

10–260. $\dfrac{(6.716)(3.2 \times 10^3)(0.0173)(413)}{(0.0000787)(6.6 \times 10^4)}$

10–261. $\dfrac{(1.061 \times 10^{-1})(96,000)(3.717)}{(7.34 \times 10^{-6})(3.9 \times 10^4)(13.5)}$

10–262. $\dfrac{(361)(482)(5.816)(38.91)(0.00616)}{(0.07181)(3 \times 10^3)(39.36)}$

Problems (continued)

10–263. $\dfrac{(0.019 \times 10^8)(111.15)(0.0168)}{(7.96)(58.6)(0.0987)(3,000)}$

10–264. $\dfrac{(21.4)(0.82)(39.6 \times 10^{-1})}{(10.86)(6.7 \times 10^{-2})(37,613)}$

10–265. $\dfrac{(63,761)(43,890)(0.00761)}{(8 \times 10^6)(0.0781)(67.17)}$

10–266. $\dfrac{(516.7)(212 \times 10^3)(0.967)(34)}{(76,516)(2 \times 10^{-6})(618)}$

10–267. $\dfrac{(5.1 \times 10^8)(370)(8.71)(3,698)}{(0.00176)(36,170)}$

10–268. $\dfrac{(59.71 \times 10^{-6})(0.00916)(0.1695)(55.61)}{(17.33 \times 10^5)(0.3165)(10.56)(1.105)}$

10–269. $\dfrac{(773.6)(57.17)(0.316)(912.3)}{(56,000)(715,000)(471.3)}$

10–270. $\dfrac{(51.33)(461.3)(919)(5.03)}{(66,000)(71.52)(0.3316)(12.39)}$

10–271. $\dfrac{(0.6617)(75.391)(0.6577)(91.33)}{(0.3305)(5.69 \times 10)(0.00317 \times 10^{-5})}$

Proportions and Ratios

A "ratio" of one number to another is the quotient of the first with respect to the second. For example, the ratio of a to b may be written as $a:b$ or $\dfrac{a}{b}$. A "proportion" is a statement that two ratios are equal. Thus, $2:3 = 6:B$ means that $\dfrac{2}{3} = \dfrac{6}{B}$.

The slide rule is quite useful in solving problems involving ratio or proportion because these fractions may be handled on any pair of matching identical scales of the rule. The C and D scales are most commonly used for this purpose.

In the example, $\dfrac{2}{3} = \dfrac{6}{B}$, 2, 3, and 6 are known values and B is unknown. The procedure to solve for B would be as follows:

1. Divide 2 by 3 (using the C and D scales). In this position the value 2 on the D scale would be located immediately beneath 3 on the C scale.

2. The equal ratio of $\dfrac{6}{B}$ would also be found on the C and D scales. The unknown value B may be read on the C scale immediately above the known value 6 on the D scale; $B = 9$.

With this particular location of the slide, every value read on the C scale bears the identical ratio of 2:3 to the number directly below it on the D scale. It is also important to remember that the cross products of a proportion are equal. In the above example, $3 \times 6 = 2 \times B$.

Examples:

a. $\dfrac{47}{21} = \dfrac{18}{A}$ *Answer,* $A = 8.04$

b. $\dfrac{0.721}{1.336} = \dfrac{B}{89.3}$ *Answer,* $B = 48.2$

c. $\dfrac{15.9}{C} = \dfrac{72.1}{166.7}$ *Answer,* $C = 36.7$

d. $\dfrac{D}{0.1156} = \dfrac{0.921}{0.473}$ *Answer,* $D = 0.225$

e. $\dfrac{42,100}{7,060} = \dfrac{E}{0.0321}$ *Answer,* $E = 0.1912$

Folded Scales

The CF and DF scales are called *folded scales.* They are identical with the C and D scales except that their indices are in a different position. On the majority of slide rules, the CF and DF scales begin at the left end with the value π, which means that their indices will be located near the center of the rule. On some rules the CF and DF scales may be folded at $\epsilon(2.718)$ or at some other number.

Since the CF and DF scales are identical in graduations with the C and D scales, they can be used in multiplication and division just as the C and D scales are. Another important fact may be noticed when the scales are examined; that is, if a number such as 2 on the C scale is set over a number such as 3 on the D scale, then 2 on the CF scale coincides with 3 on the DF scale. This means that operations may be begun or answers obtained on either the C and D scales or on the CF and DF scales.

For example, if we wish to multiply 2 by 6, and we set the left index of the C scale over 2 on the D scale, we observe that the product cannot be read on the D scale because 6 on the C scale projects past the right end of the rule. Ordinarily this would mean that the slide would need to be run to the left so that the right index of the C scale could be used. However, by using the folded scales, we notice that the 6 on the CF scale coincides with 12 on the DF scale, thereby eliminating an extra movement of the slide (See Figure 10–19). In many cases the use of the folded scales will reduce the number of times the slide must be shifted to the left because an answer would fall beyond the right end of the D scale.

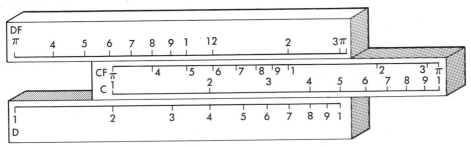

Figure 10–19.

There are several methods by which the location of the decimal point in the answer can be determined. The decimal point location can best be found by using the method of scientific notation.

The projection rule can be used if it is always remembered that an answer read on the DF scale to the right of the index (near the center of the rule) corresponds to a left projection. Since in many operations the decimal point location in the answer can be determined by inspection, the decimal point can often be placed without reference to projection rules.

A convenient method of multiplying or dividing by π is afforded by the use of the folded scales. For example, to find the product 2π, set the hairline over 2 on the D scale. The product 6.28 is read on the DF scale under the hairline. Of course this same operation may be performed by using either index of the slide.

Reciprocal Scales

The CI, DI, and CIF scales are known as *reciprocal scales* or *inverted scales*. They are identical with the C, D, and CF scales, respectively, except that they are inverted; that is, the numbers represented by the graduations on these scales increase from right to left. On some slide rules, the inverted scale graduations are printed in red to help distinguish them from the other scale markings.

An important principle to remember when using these scales is that a number on the C scale will have its reciprocal in the same position on the CI scale. Conversely, when the hairline is set to a number on the CI scale, its reciprocal is under the hairline on the C scale.

The inverted scales are useful in problems involving repeated multiplication or division because some movements of the slide may be eliminated.

Example: Find the product:

$$(1.71)(8.30)(0.252)(4910)(53.8)$$

In order to perform this operation, using the inverted scales, the following steps are used:

1. Set the hairline to 1.71 on the D scale.
2. Move the slide until 83 on the CI scale is under the hairline.
3. Move the hairline until it is set on 252 on the C scale.
4. Move the slide until 491 on the CI scale is under the hairline.
5. Move the hairline until it is set on 538 on the C scale.
6. Read the product 94600 under the hairline on the D scale.

The actual process has involved the use of reciprocal quantities in division in Steps 2 and 4 of the sequence above. Rewritten as the operation is actually performed, the problem appears as follows:

$$\frac{(1.71)(0.252)(53.8)}{(1/8.30)(1/4910)}$$

ESTIMATION OF ANSWER BY SCIENTIFIC NOTATION:

$(2)(8)(2)(10)^{-1}(5)(10)^{3}(5)(10)^{1} = \underline{\underline{(8)(10)^{5}}} \leftarrow$ ESTIMATED ANSWER

Since the digits read on the slide rule were 946, the actual product would be $9.46(10)^5$. The projection rule should not be used with inverted scales, since the number of left projections are sometimes difficult to determine.

Proper use of the folded and inverted scales will enable one to work each practice problem below with only one setting of the slide.

Use of Folded and Reciprocal Scales Practice Problems

10–272. $(264)(564)(522) = (7.77)(10)^7$

10–273. $(387)(7.32)(176) = (4.99)(10)^5$

10–274. $(0.461)(4.79)(1140) = (2.52)(10)^3$

10–275. $(6.69)(1548)(92,000) = (9.53)(10)^8$

10–276. $(561)(3.30)(1.94) = (3.59)(10)^3$

10–277. $(1456)(0.351)(0.835) = (4.27)(10)^2$

10–278. $(1262)(0.405)(65,100) = (3.33)(10)^7$

10–279. $(0.1871)(5.04)(53,000) = (5.00)(10)^4$

10–280. $(7.28 \times 10^{-5})(4.16)(14.10) = (4.27)(10)^{-3}$

10–281. $(10.70)(19,400)(0.0914) = (1.897)(10)^4$

10–282. $(4.56)(47.4)(87.1) = (1.883)(10)^4$

10–283. $(0.510)(68.9)(3,370) = (1.184)(10)^5$

10–284. $(2,030)(14.72)(129.7) = (3.88)(10)^6$

10–285. $(1824)(29.1)(21,800) = (1.157)(10)^9$

10–286. $(0.0255)(0.0932)(0.867) = (2.06)(10)^{-3}$

10–287. $(93.6)(3.99)(5,680) = (2.12)(10)^6$

10–288. $(4.48)(103.5)(0.198) = (9.18)(10)^1$

10–289. $(0.580)(43,700)(40.3) = (1.021)(10)^6$

10–290. $(7.05)(62.0)(34.9) = (1.525)(10)^4$

10–291. $(74.8)(8.)(483,000) = (2.89)(10)^8$

10–292. $\dfrac{(208)(90.2)}{(30,600)} = (6.13)(10)^{-1}$

10–293. $\dfrac{(0.387)(25,200)}{(0.118)} = (8.26)(10)^4$

10–294. $\dfrac{(0.458)(14.05 \times 10^{-15})}{(75.5 \times 10^8)} = (8.52)(10)^{-25}$

10–295. $\dfrac{(18,100)(84.4)}{(10.92)} = (1.40)(10)^5$

10–296. $\dfrac{(477)(9,720)}{(19,150)} = (2.42)(10)^2$

10–297. $\dfrac{(25,600)}{(68,500)(12,080)} = (3.09)(10)^{-5}$

10–298. $\dfrac{(3050)(1.00 \times 10^{-20})}{(71.4)(0.946)} = (4.52)(10)^{-19}$

10–299. $\dfrac{(1,670)}{(0.000570)(24,700)} = (1.186)(10)^2$

10–300. $\dfrac{(51.5)}{(15.14)(0.00194)} = (1.753)(10)^3$

10–301. $\dfrac{(917,000)}{(54.3)(119.8 \times 10^{-4})} = (1.41)(10)^6$

Squares and Square Roots

The A and B scales have been constructed so that their lengths are one-half those of the C and D scales (see Figure 10–20). Similarly some slide rules are so constructed that they have a scale (Sq 1 and Sq 2, or R_1 and R_2) which is twice as long as the D scale. This means that the logarithm of 3 as represented on the D

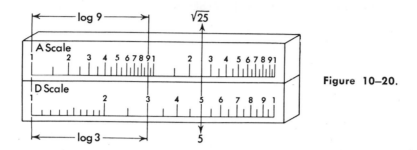

Figure 10–20.

scale would be equivalent in length to the logarithm of 9 on the A scale. Where the Sq 1 and Sq 2 or the R_1 and R_2 scales are used in conjunction with the D scale, the logarithm of 3 on the Sq 2 (R_2) scale would be equivalent in length to the logarithm of 9 on the D scale.

To Find the Square Root of a Number Using the A and D Scales

1. Get an estimate of the intended answer by placing a bar over every two digits, starting at the decimal point and working outward. There will be a digit in the answer for each bar marked.

2. Set the number on the A scale and read the square root on the D scale under the hairline. Note that the estimated answer will always indicate which A scale to use, since only one of the scales will give a square root near the estimated value.

Greater accuracy can be obtained by using the D scale in conjunction with the Sq 1 and Sq 2 scales (R_1 and R_2).

Examples for Finding the Location of Decimal Points:

a. $\sqrt{\overline{97}\ \overline{65}}$ The estimated answer is somewhere between 90 and 100.

$\overset{9\quad x}{}$

b. $\sqrt{\overline{.00}\ \overline{30}}$ The estimated answer is approximately 0.05.

$\overset{.\ 0\quad 5}{}$

NOTE: In the last example, since the given value was 0.003, an extra zero would have to be added after the 3 to complete the digits beneath the bar.

Examples for Finding the Square Root of a Number:

a. $\sqrt{\overset{1}{1}\ \overset{x}{03}\ \overset{x}{57}}$ The estimated answer is somewhere between 100 and 200.

$\sqrt{1\ 03\ 57} = 101.8 = \underline{1.018 \times 10^2}$

b. $\sqrt{\overset{0.\ 0}{0.00}\ \overset{2}{05}\ \overset{x}{20}}$ The estimated answer is approximately 0.02.

$\sqrt{0.00\ 05\ 20} = 0.02280 = \underline{2.280 \times 10^{-2}}$

Examples for Finding Squares:

1. Express the number in scientific notation.

   a. $(0.0000956)^2 = (9.56 \times 10^{-5})^2$

2. Square each part of the converted term by setting the number to be squared on the D scale and reading its square on the A scale under the hairline.

   a. $(9.56)^2 \times (10^{-5})^2 = 91.4 \times 10^{-10} = \underline{9.14 \times 10^{-9}}$

   b. $(90100)^2 = (9.01 \times 10^4)^2$
   $(9.01)^2 \times (10^4)^2 = 81 \times 10^8 = \underline{8.1 \times 10^9}$

   c. $(357000000)^2 = (3.57 \times 10^8)^2$
   $(3.57)^2 \times (10^8)^2 = 12.7 \times 10^{16} = \underline{1.27 \times 10^{17}}$

   d. $(0.00000001050)^2 = (1.05 \times 10^{-8})^2$
   $(1.05)^2 \times (10^{-8})^2 = \underline{1.10 \times 10^{-16}}$

Squares and Square Roots Practice Problems

10–302. $(408)^2 = (1.665)(10)^5$

10–303. $(8.35)^2 = (6.97)(10)^1$

10–304. $(3,980)^2 = (1.584)(10)^7$

10–305. $(0.941)^2 = (8.85)(10)^{-1}$

10–306. $(57.4)^2 = (3.29)(10)^3$

10–307. $(0.207)^2 = (4.28)(10)^{-2}$

10–308. $(784)^2 = (6.15)(10)^5$

10–309. $(296,000)^2 = (8.76)(10)^{10}$

10–310. $(1037)^2 = (1.075)(10)^6$

10–311. $(8.93)^2 = (7.97)(10)^1$

10–312. $(30.9)^2 = (9.55)(10)^2$

10–313. $(43,300)^2 = (1.875)(10)^9$

10–314. $(0.00609)^2 = (3.71)(10)^{-5}$

10–315. $(0.846)^2 = (7.16)(10)^{-1}$

10–316. $(55.2 \times 10^3)^2 = (3.05)(10)^9$

10–317. $(0.0707)^2 = (5.00)(10)^{-3}$

10–318. $(11.92 \times 10^{-4})^2 = (1.421)(10)^{-6}$

10–319. $(0.291 \times 10^{-5})^2 = (8.47)(10)^{-12}$

10–320. $(449,000)^2 = (2.02)(10)^{11}$

10–321. $(0.000977)^2 = (9.55)(10)^{-7}$

10–322. $(33.5 \times 10^{-6})^2 = (1.122)(10)^{-9}$

10–323. $(8,810)^2 = (7.76)(10)^7$

10–324. $(50.9 \times 10^6)^2 = (2.59)(10)^{15}$

10–325. $(99,300)^2 = (9.86)(10)^9$

10–326. $(0.0714 \times 10^{-6})^2 = (5.10)(10)^{-15}$

10–327. $\sqrt{96,100} = (3.10)(10)^2$

10–328. $\sqrt{0.912} = (9.55)(10)^{-1}$

10–329. $\sqrt{24.9} = 4.99$

10–330. $\sqrt{0.01124} = (1.06)(10)^{-1}$

10–331. $\sqrt{5,256} = (7.25)(10)^1$

10–332. $\sqrt{0.3764} = (6.14)(10)^{-1}$

10–333. $\sqrt{43,800,000} = (6.62)(10)^3$

10–334. $\sqrt{0.01369} = (1.17)(10)^{-1}$

10–335. $\sqrt{73.6} = 8.58$

10–336. $\sqrt{1.1025} = 1.05$

10–337. $\sqrt{487,000} = (6.98)(10)^2$

10–338. $\sqrt{580.8} = (2.41)(10)^1$

10–339. $\sqrt{0.00002767} = (5.26)(10)^{-3}$

10–340. $\sqrt{0.1399} = (3.74)(10)^{-1}$

10–341. $\sqrt{6,368} = (7.98)(10)^1$

10–342. $\sqrt{1.142 \times 10^{-3}} = (3.38)(10)^{-2}$

10–343. $\sqrt{6.496 \times 10^1} = 8.06$

10–344. $\sqrt{190,970} = (4.37)(10)^2$

10–345. $\sqrt{3,204,000} = (1.79)(10)^3$

10–346. $\sqrt{0.003807} = (6.17)(10)^{-2}$

10–347. $\sqrt{0.08352} = (2.89)(10)^{-1}$

10–348. $\sqrt{3069} = (5.54)(10)^1$

10–349. $\sqrt{61.78 \times 10^{-4}} = (7.86)(10)^{-2}$

10–350. $\sqrt{3.648 \times 10^{-8}} = (1.91)(10)^{-4}$

10–351. $\sqrt{9.92 \times 10^5} = (9.96)(10)^2$

Problems

Solve by method of squares and square roots.

10–352. $(1468.)^2$

10–353. $(0.886)^2$

10–354. $(67.4)^2$

10–355. $(11.96)^2$

10–356. $(0.00448)^2$

10–357. $(0.000551)^2$

10–358. $(9.22)^2$

10–359. $(64,800.)^2$

10–360. $(0.0668)^2$

10–361. $(16.85)^2$

10–362. $(1.802 \times 10^9)^2$

10–363. $(0.00358)^2$

10–364. $(5089)^2$

10–365. $(44,900.)^2$

10–366. $(64.88)^2$

10–367. $\sqrt{11.81}$

10–368. $\sqrt{4567.}$

10–369. $\sqrt{0.01844}$

10–370. $\sqrt{0.9953}$

10–371. $\sqrt{1395.}$

10–372. $\sqrt{0.0001288}$

10–373. $\sqrt{1.082 \times 10^2}$

10–374. $\sqrt{75.9}$

10–375. $\sqrt{\pi}$

10–376. $\sqrt{73,800}$.

10–377. $\sqrt{13.38}$

10–378. $\sqrt{93.07}$

10–379. $\sqrt{0.1148}$

10–380. $\sqrt{0.2776}$

10–381. $\sqrt{9.31}$

10–382. $(0.774)^2(11.47)^{1/2}$

10–383. $(0.1442)^{1/2}(33.89)^{1/2}$

10–384. $(54.23)^2(88,900)^{1/2}$

10–385. $\sqrt{234.5}\ \sqrt{55,900}$.

10–386. $\sqrt{16.38}\ \sqrt{45.6}\ \sqrt{0.9}$

10–387. $\sqrt{415}.\ \sqrt{\pi}\ \sqrt{86.4}$

10–388. $\sqrt{15.66}\ \sqrt{0.1904}\ \sqrt{\pi}$

10–389. $(34.77)^2(54.8)^2(0.772)^{1/2}$

10–390. $\sqrt{7.90}\ \sqrt{7.02}\ \sqrt{11.54}$

10–391. $\sqrt{31.19}\ \sqrt{56.7}\ \sqrt{54.8}$

Cubes and Cube Roots

The D and K scales are used to find the cube or cube root of a number as shown in Figure 10–21. The same general procedure is used as that followed for squaring

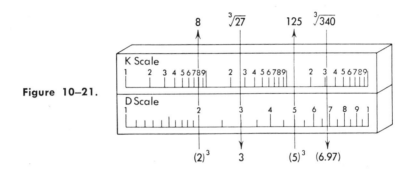

Figure 10–21.

numbers and taking the square root of a number. The K scale is divided into scales K_1, K_2, and K_3, which are each one-third the length of the D scale. Thus, if a number is located on the D scale, the cube of the number will be indicated on the K scale. It follows that if a number is located on one of the K scales, the root of the number would appear on the D scale.

To Find the Cube Root of a Number

1. Get an estimate of the intended answer by placing a bar over every three digits, starting at the decimal point and working outward. There will be a digit in the answer for each bar marked.

2. Set the number on the K scale and read the cube root on the D scale under the hairline. (Some slide rules, such as those made by Pickett, have three cube root scales instead of the conventional K scale. These cube root scales are used with the D scale to determine cubes and cube roots of numbers. When they are used, however, the number should be set on the D scale and the cube root read on the appropriate cube root scale.)

Examples for Finding the Location of Decimal Points:

$$\overset{\text{3}\quad\text{x.}}{a.\;\sqrt[3]{44,\ 800.}}$$ The estimated answer is somewhere between 30 and 40.

$$\overset{\text{0.}\quad\text{0}\quad\text{2}}{b.\;\sqrt[3]{0.\ 000\ 011}}$$ The estimated answer is approximately 0.02.

NOTE: In estimating the answer by marking bars over the digit groupings, be sure that the bars cover three digits instead of two, as was the case in square roots.

Since an estimated answer [see Example *a.* above] has been obtained, it is easy to pick the proper K scale (K_1, K_2, or K_3) to use. Remember that only one of these will give an answer between 30 and 40 [see Example *a.*].

Examples for Finding the Cube Roots of a Number:

$$\overset{\text{1}\quad\text{x}\quad\text{x}}{a.\;\sqrt[3]{1\ 490\ 000.}}$$ The estimated answer is somewhere between 100 and 200.

$$\sqrt[3]{1\ 490\ 000.} = 114.1 = \underline{(1.141)(10)^2}.$$

$$\overset{\text{0.}\quad\text{0}\quad\text{6}}{b.\;\sqrt[3]{0.\ 000\ 156\ 9}}$$ The estimated answer is approximately 0.06.

$$\sqrt[3]{0.\ 000\ 156\ 9} = 0.0537 = \underline{(5.37)(10)^{-2}}.$$

Examples for Finding Cubes:

1. Convert the number to a number between 1 and 10 (scientific notation) that must be multiplied by 10 raised to some power.

    a. $(0.00641)^3 = (6.41 \times 10^{-3})^3$

2. Cube each part of the converted term by setting the number to be cubed on the D scale and reading its cube on the K scale under the hairline.

    a. $(6.41 \times 10^{-3})^3 = (264)(10)^{-9} = \underline{2.63 \times 10^{-7}}$

    b. $(93.88)^3 = (9.388 \times 10^1)^3$
       $(9.388)^3(10^1)^3 = 830 \times 10^3 = \underline{8.27 \times 10^5}$

    c. $(2,618,000.)^3 = (2.618 \times 10^6)^3$
       $(2.618)^3(10^6)^3 = (17.95 \times 10)^{18} = \underline{1.794 \times 10^{19}}$

    d. $(0.000001194)^3 = (1.194 \times 10^{-6})^3$
       $(1.194)^3(10^{-6})^3 = \underline{1.701 \times 10^{-18}}$

Cubes and Cube Roots Practice Problems

10-392. $(206)^3 = (8.74)(10)^6$

10-393. $(7.68)^3 = (4.53)(10)^2$

10-394. $(0.00519)^3 = (1.398)(10)^{-7}$

10-395. $(33.5)^3 = (3.76)(10)^4$

10-396. $(0.229)^3 = (1.201)(10)^{-2}$

10-397. $(1090)^3 = (1.295)(10)^9$

10-398. $(0.0579)^3 = (1.94)(10)^{-4}$

10-399. $(9.89)^3 = (9.67)(10)^2$

10-400. $(419)^3 = (7.36)(10)^7$

10-401. $(52.4)^3 = (1.439)(10)^5$

10-402. $(0.0249)^3 = (1.544)(10)^{-5}$

10-403. $(14.9)^3 = (3.31)(10)^3$

10-404. $(2.96)^3 = (2.59)(10)^1$

10-405. $(397)^3 = (6.26)(10)^7$

10-406. $(63.4)^3 = (2.55)(10)^5$

10-407. $(9040)^3 = (7.39)(10)^{11}$

10-408. $(0.0783)^3 = (4.80)(10)^{-4}$

10-409. $(0.844)^3 = (6.01)(10)^{-1}$

10-410. $(5.41)^3 = (1.583)(10)^2$

10-411. $(35.5)^3 = (4.47)(10)^4$

10-412. $(0.1270)^3 = (2.05)(10)^{-3}$

10-413. $(20.7)^3 = (8.87)(10)^3$

10-414. $(691)^3 = (3.30)(10)^8$

10-415. $(0.719)^3 = (3.72)(10)^{-1}$

10-416. $(4.34)^3 = (8.17)(10)^1$

10-417. $\sqrt[3]{30,960,000} = (3.14)(10)^2$

10-418. $\sqrt[3]{0.001728} = (1.20)(10)^{-1}$

10-419. $\sqrt[3]{491} = 7.89$

10-420. $\sqrt[3]{9.91 \times 10^{11}} = (9.97)(10)^3$

10-421. $\sqrt[3]{0.272} = (6.48)(10)^{-1}$

10-422. $\sqrt[3]{118,400} = (4.91)(10)^1$

10-423. $\sqrt[3]{22.91} = 2.84$

10-424. $\sqrt[3]{527,500} = (8.08)(10)^1$

10-425. $\sqrt[3]{1.295} = 1.09$

10-426. $\sqrt[3]{0.0001804} = (5.65)(10)^{-2}$

10-427. $\sqrt[3]{460,100,000} = (7.72)(10)^2$

10-428. $\sqrt[3]{261,000} = (6.39)(10)^1$

10-429. $\sqrt[3]{0.11620} = (4.88)(10)^{-1}$

10-430. $\sqrt[3]{0.0030486} = (1.45)(10)^{-1}$

10-431. $\sqrt[3]{0.03096} = (3.14)(10)^{-1}$

10-432. $\sqrt[3]{504.4} = 7.96$

10-433. $\sqrt[3]{8,869,000} = (2.07)(10)^2$

10-434. $\sqrt[3]{174,700,000} = (5.59)(10)^2$

10-435. $\sqrt[3]{5.886 \times 10^{10}} = (3.89)(10)^3$

10-436. $\sqrt[3]{5.885 \times 10^{-1}} = (8.38)(10)^{-1}$

10-437. $\sqrt[3]{76.105 \times 10^{-5}} = (9.13)(10)^{-2}$

10-438. $\sqrt[3]{327.1} = 6.89$

10-439. $\sqrt[3]{0.02567} = (2.95)(10)^{-1}$

10-440. $\sqrt[3]{0.0004118} = (7.44)(10)^{-2}$

10-441. $\sqrt[3]{68,420} = (4.09)(10)^1$

Problems

Solve by Method of Cubes and Cube Roots.

10–442. $(86)^3$

10–443. $(148)^3$

10–444. $(395,000)^3$

10–445. $(47.6)^3$

10–446. $(1.074)^3$

10–447. $(76.9)^3$

10–448. $(220.8)^3$

10–449. $(9.72)^3$

10–450. $(110.7)^3$

10–451. $(91.3)^3$

10–452. $(1.757 \times 10^4)^3$

10–453. $(3.06 \times 10^{-7})^3$

10–454. $(44.8 \times 10^{-1})^3$

10–455. $(0.933 \times 10^{-2})^3$

10–456. $(0.1184 \times 10^8)^3$

10–457. $(51.5 \times 10^2)^3$

10–458. $\sqrt[3]{118}$

10–459. $\sqrt[3]{2,197}$

10–460. $\sqrt[3]{9}$

10–461. $\sqrt[3]{0.0689}$

10–462. $\sqrt[3]{0.001338}$

10–463. $\sqrt[3]{0.1794}$

10–464. $\sqrt[3]{0.0891}$

10–465. $\sqrt[3]{34,690.}$

10–466. $\sqrt[3]{0.3329}$

10–467. $\sqrt[3]{1,258,000}$

10–468. $\sqrt[3]{0.1853}$

10–469. $\sqrt[3]{12.88}$

10–470. $\sqrt[3]{4.98 \times 10^7}$

10–471. $\sqrt[3]{1.844 \times 10^{-5}}$

10–472. $\sqrt[3]{3.86 \times 10^{-1}}$

10–473. $(9.94)(0.886)^{1/3}$

10–474. $(248.)(11.98)^{1/3}$

10–475. $(0.117)(0.0964)^{1/3}$

10–476. $(\pi)^3(44.89)^3$

10–477. $(6.88)^3(0.00799)^3$

10–478. $(0.915)^{1/3}(0.366)^{1/3}\sqrt[3]{11,250}(36.12)^{1/3}$

10–479. $(2.34)^3(3.34)^3(4.56)^3(5.67)^3$

10–480. $(8.26)^{1/3}(8.26)^3(1000)^{1/3}(10)^3$

10–481. $\sqrt[3]{2670}$ $\sqrt[3]{3165}$ $\sqrt[3]{1065}$ $\sqrt[3]{7776}$

10–482. $\sqrt[3]{206}$ $\sqrt[3]{0.791}(12.35)^3(26.3)^3$

Trigonometric Functions

Finding trigonometric functions on a log-log rule is a rather simple process. The angle may be read on the S (sine), ST (sine and tangent of small angles), or T (tangent) scales. The functions may be read under the hairline on the C, D, or DI scales without any movement of the slide.

Sine 0° to 0.574°. It is not often that the student needs to know the function of extremely small angles, but if he does need them, it is possible to get approximate values for these functions without consulting tables.

Method 1: (Based upon the relation that the sine of small angles is approximately equal to the size of the angle expressed in radians)

1. This method is more accurate than the following Method 2, and is preferable.
2. Express the angle in question in degrees.
3. Change the degrees to radians by dividing by 57.3.

NOTE: $57.3° = 1$ radian (approximately)

4. The value obtained is the approximate answer.

Example:

$$\sin 6' = ?$$
$$6' = \tfrac{6}{60} = 0.10°$$
$$\sin 6' = \frac{0.10}{57.3}$$
$$\sin 6' = 0.00174 \text{ approximately}$$

Method 2:

1. Keep in mind the following values:

$$\sin 1'' = 0.000005 \text{ (five zeros-five) approximately}$$
$$\sin 1' = 0.0003 \text{ (three zeros-three) approximately}$$

2. For small angles, multiply the value of $1'$ or $1''$, as the case may be, by the number of minutes or seconds in question.

Example:

$$\sin 6' = ?$$
$$\sin 6' = (6)(\sin 1')$$
$$\sin 6' = (6)(0.0003)$$
$$\sin 6' = 0.0018 \text{ approximately}$$

Sine 0.574° to 5.74°. To find the sine of an angle between 0.574° and 5.74°, the ST and D scales are used as shown in Figure 10–22.

Example: $\sin 1.5° = ?$

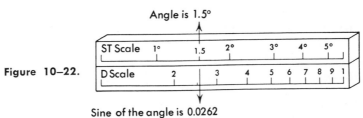

Angle is 1.5°

Figure 10–22.

Sine of the angle is 0.0262

INSTRUCTIONS

1. Be certain that the left index of the D scale is directly under the left index of the ST scale.
2. Set the hairline to the angle on the ST scale.
3. Read the answer on the D scale. The answer will be a decimal number and will have one zero preceding the digits read from the rule.

Sine 5.74° to 90°. To find the sine of an angle between 5.74° and 90°, the S and D scales are used as shown in Figure 10–23.

Example: $\sin 45° = ?$

Angle is 45°

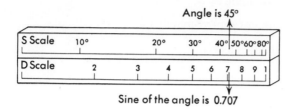

Figure 10–23.

Sine of the angle is 0.707

INSTRUCTIONS:

1. Be certain that the left index of the D scale is directly under the left index of the S scale.

2. Set the hairline to the angle on the S scale. If the rule has more than one set of figures on the S scale, the angles for sine functions are usually shown to the right of the longer graduations.

3. Read the answer on the D scale. Place the decimal preceding the first digit read from the rule.

Sines Practice Problems

10–483. Sin 26° = 0.438

10–484. Sin 81° = 0.988

10–485. Sin 16° = 0.276

10–486. Sin 15.5° = 0.267

10–487. Sin 42.6° = 0.677

10–488. Sin 3.33° = 0.0581

10–489. Sin 10.17° = 0.1765

10–490. Sin 63.2° = 0.893

10–491. Sin 70.83° = 0.945

10–492. Sin 26.67° = 0.449

10–493. Sin 7.33° = 0.1276

10–494. Sin 2.83° = 0.0494

10–495. Sin 51.5° = 0.783

10–496. Sin 5.17° = 0.0901

10–497. Sin 33.8° = 0.556

10–498. Sin 20.3° = 0.348

10–499. Sin 68.2° = 0.928

10–500. Arc Sin 0.557 = 33.8°

10–501. Sin⁻¹ 0.032 = 1.83°

10–502. Sin⁻¹ 0.242 = 14.0°

10–503. Arc Sin 0.709 = 45.15°

10–504. Sin⁻¹ 0.581 = 35.5°

10–505. Arc Sin 0.999 = 87.5°

10–506. Sin⁻¹ 0.569 = 34.68°

10–507. Sin⁻¹ 0.401 = 23.6°

Cosine 0° to 84.26°. To find the cosine of an angle between 0° and 84.26°, the markings to the left of the long graduations on the S scale are used in conjunction with the D scale. Note that the markings begin with 0° at the right end of the scale and progress to 84.26° at the left end of the scale as shown in Figure 10–24.

Example: $\cos 74.1° = ?$

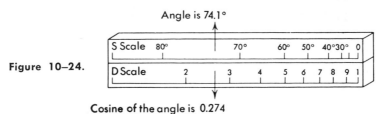

Angle is 74.1°

Figure 10–24.

Cosine of the angle is 0.274

Cosine 84.26° to 89.4°. To find the cosine of an angle between 84.26° and 89.4°, the complement of the angle on the ST scale is used in conjunction with the D scale.

Example:
$$\cos 88.5° = ?$$
$$\text{complement of } 88.5° = 1.5°$$
$$\sin 1.5° = 0.0262$$
$$\cos 88.5° = 0.0262$$

Cosine 89.4° to 90°. To find the cosine of an angle between 89.4° and 90°, determine the complement of the angle and find the value of the sine of this angle as previously discussed.

Example:
$$\cos 89.94° = ?$$
$$\text{complement of } 89.94° = 0.06°$$
$$\sin 0.06° = \frac{0.06}{57.3} = 0.001048$$
$$\cos 89.94° = 0.001048$$

NOTE: In finding the cosine of any angle, it is sometimes more convenient to look up the sine of the complement of the angle.

Example:
$$\cos 60° = ?$$
$$\text{complement of } 60° = 30°$$
$$\sin 30° = 0.500$$

Therefore,
$$\cos 60° = 0.500$$

Cosines Practice Problems

10–508. Cos 18.8° = 0.947

10–509. Cos 33.17° = 0.837

10–510. Cos 71.5° = 0.317

10–511. Cos 45° = 0.707

10–512. Cos 68.3° = 0.370

10–513. Cos 26.9° = 0.892

10–514. Cos 55.7° = 0.564

10–515. Cos 5.5° = 0.995

10–516. Cos 81.3° = 0.151

10–517. Cos 8.9° = 0.988

10–518. Cos 77.6° = 0.215

10–519. Cos 39.1° = 0.776

10–520. Cos 50.7° = 0.633

10–521. Cos 11.5° = 0.980

10–522. Cos 49.2° = 0.653

10–523. Arc Cos 0.901 = 25.7°

10–524. Cos⁻¹ 0.727 = 43.4°

10–525. Cos⁻¹ 0.0814 = 85.3°

Cosines Practice Problems (continued)

10–526. Arc Cos 0.284 = 73.5°
10–527. Cos⁻¹ 0.585 = 54.2°
10–528. Cos⁻¹ 0.658 = 48.8°
10–529. Cos⁻¹ 0.1190 = 83.1°

10–530. Arc Cos 0.303 = 72.4°
10–531. Cos⁻¹ 0.505 = 59.7°
10–532. Cos⁻¹ 0.693 = 46.1°

Tangent 0° to 5.74°. For small angles (0° to 5.74°) the tangent of the angle may be considered to be the same value as the sine of that angle.

Tangent 5.74° to 45°. To find the tangent of an angle between 5.74° and 45°, the T scale is used in conjunction with the D scale, as shown in Figure 10–25.

Example: Find tan 30°.

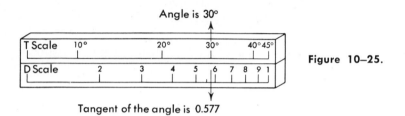

Figure 10–25.

INSTRUCTIONS

1. Be certain that the left index of the D scale is directly under the left index of the T scale.

2. Set the hairline to the angle on the T scale. If the T scale has more than one set of markings, be certain that the correct markings are used.

3. Read the answer on the D scale. Place the decimal preceding the first digit read from the rule.

Tangent 45° to 84.26°. To find the tangent of an angle between 45° and 84.26°, the markings to the left of the longer graduations on the T scale are used in conjunction with the CI or DI scales, as shown in Figure 10–26.

Example: tan 70° = ?

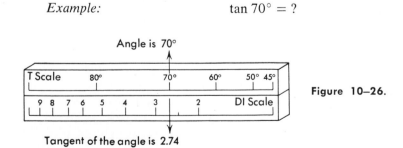

Figure 10–26.

INSTRUCTIONS

1. Be certain that the left index of the DI or CI scale is aligned with the left index of the T scale.

2. Set the hairline to the angle on the T scale.

3. Read the answer on the CI or DI scale. Note that these scales read from right to left. Place the decimal after the first digit read from the rule.

Tangent 84.26° to 89.426°. To find the tangent of an angle between 84.26° and 89.426°, the complement of the angle on the ST scale is used in conjunction with the CI or DI scales, as shown in Figure 10–27.

Example: $\qquad$ tan 88° = ?

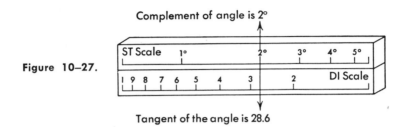

Figure 10–27.

INSTRUCTIONS

1. Be certain that the left index of the DI or CI scale is aligned with the left index of the ST scale.

2. Complement of 88° = 2°.

3. Read the answer on the DI or CI scale. Note that these scales read from right to left.

4. Place the decimal point after the first two digits read from the rule.

Frequently the value of the function of an angle is known and it is desired to find the value of the angle.

Example: $\qquad$ $\sin \theta = 0.53;$
$$\theta = ?$$

This may be written in the inverse form in either of two ways:

$$\text{Arc sin } 0.53 = \theta$$

or $\qquad\qquad\qquad\qquad$ $\text{Sin}^{-1} 0.53 = \theta$

then $\qquad\qquad\qquad\qquad$ $\theta = 32°$

The forms arc sin, arc cos, and arc tan are usually preferred in modern practice.

Tangents Practice Problems

10–533. Tan 29.6° = 0.568

10–534. Tan 48.2° = 1.118

10–535. Tan 11.5° = 0.203

10–536. Tan 71.9° = 3.06

10–537. Tan 5.7° = 0.0993

10–538. Tan 61.4° = 1.834

10–539. Tan 33.3° = 0.657

10–540. Tan 69.2° = 2.63

10–541. Tan 40.6° = 0.857

10–542. Tan 8.7° = 0.1530

10–543. Tan 17.5° = 0.315

10–544. Tan 85.1° = 11.66

10–545. Tan 58.6° = 1.638

10–546. Tan 39.3° = 0.818

10–547. Tan 20.9° = 0.382

10–548. Tan 42.1° = 0.904

10–549. Arc tan 0.362 = 19.9°

10–550. Arc tan 0.841 = 40.1°

10–551. Tan^{-1} 0.119 = 6.78°

10–552. Tan^{-1} 0.0721 = 4.13°

10–553. Tan^{-1} 1.732 = 60°

10–554. Arc tan 21.6 = 87.3°

10–555. Tan^{-1} 0.776 = 37.8°

10–556 Arc tan 89.3 = 89.36°

10–557. Tan^{-1} 0.661 = 33.5°

The following tables have been prepared for reference purposes. The student should check all the examples with his rule as he proceeds.

	ANGLE	READ ANGLE ON	READ FUNCTION ON	DECIMAL	EXAMPLES
sine or tangent	0°–0.574° Convert the angle to radians (1 radian = 57.3°), and this value is assumed to be equal to the sine or tangent of the angle.				
sine or tangent	0.574°–5.74°	ST	D	0.0xxx	tan 2° = 0.0349 sin 3° = 0.0523
sine	5.74°–90°	S (right markings)	D	0.xxxx	sin 29° = 0.485
cosine	0°–84.26°	S (left markings)	D	0.xxxx	cos 43° = 0.7314
tangent	5.74°–45°	T (right markings)	D	0.xxxx	tan 13° = 0.231
tangent	45°–84.26°	T (left markings)	DI	x.xxx	tan 78° = 4.70
tangent	84.26°–89.426	Set complement on ST	DI	xx.xxx	tan 89° = 57.3
cosecant	5.74°–90°	S (right markings)	DI	x.xxx	csc 63° = 1.122
secant	0°–84.26°	S (left markings)	DI	x.xxx	sec 48° = 1.494
cotangent	0.574°–5.74°	ST	DI	xx.xx	cot 3.5° = 16.35
cotangent	5.74°–45°	T (right markings)	DI	x.xxx	cot 23° = 2.36
cotangent	45°–84.26°	T (left markings)	D	0.xxxx	cot 68° = 0.404

Trigonometric Functions: Problems

Solve, using the slide rule.

10–558. sin 35°
10–559. sin 14°
10–560. sin 78°
10–561. sin 3.7°
10–562. sin 88.3°
10–563. sin 55.3°
10–564. cos 35°
10–565. cos 66°
10–566. cos 21.3°
10–567. cos 11.1°
10–568. cos 7.9°
10–569. cos 43.8°
10–570. tan 33.8°
10–571. tan 9.4°
10–572. tan 37.7°
10–573. tan 22.5°
10–574. tan 86.1°
10–575. tan 54.4°
10–576. tan 70.3°
10–577. tan 29.7°
10–578. tan 36.5°
10–579. tan 13.3°
10–580. tan 45.8°
10–581. cot 14.7°
10–582. cot 81.8°
10–583. cot 36.9°
10–584. cot 61.2°
10–585. cot 54.3°

10–586. cot 18.7°
10–587. cot 3.77°
10–588. cot 66.4°
10–589. csc 38.1°
10–590. csc 75.2°
10–591. csc 88.3°
10–592. csc 12.8°
10–593. csc 46.4°
10–594. csc 81.1°
10–595. csc 32.6°
10–596. csc 9.03°
10–597. sec 6.14°
10–598. sec 59.2°
10–599. sec 79.4°
10–600. sec 19.5°
10–601. sec 2.77°
10–602. sec 45.9°
10–603. arc-sin 0.771
10–604. arc cos 0.119
10–605. arc tan 34.8
10–606. arc sec 7.18
10–607. arc csc 1.05
10–608. cos 33.4°
10–609. cos 3.6°
10–610. arc cos 0.992
10–611. cos 24.67°
10–612. $\cos^{-1} 0.496$
10–613. cos 36°6′

10–614. arc cos 0.238
10–615. cos 0.75°
10–616. cos 36.6°
10–617. tan 32.6°
10–618. tan 16.34°
10–619. tan 88°30′
10–620. arc tan 0.62
10–621. $\tan^{-1} 0.75$
10–622. arc tan 0.392
10–623. $\tan^{-1} 1.53$
10–624. tan 37°24′
10–625. arc tan 0.567
10–626. $\tan^{-1} 0.0321$
10–627. cot 19°33′
10–628. sec 46°46′
10–629. csc 32°12′
10–630. sin 37°
10–631. sin 51°50′
10–632. sin 68°37′
10–633. sin 75°10′
10–634. arc sin 0.622
10–635. sin 13.6°
10–636. $\sin^{-1} 0.068$
10–637. sin 14.6°
10–638. arc sin 0.169
10–639. sin 34.67°
10–640. cos 26.26°
10–641. csc 20°20′

10–642. $(\csc 20°)(\sin 46°)$
10–643. $(\cos 32°)(\tan 43°)$
10–644. $\dfrac{(\sin 13.9°)}{(\cot 13.9°)}$
10–645. $\dfrac{\cot 33°22'}{\sec 4°53'}$
10–646. $\dfrac{(\cos 33°15')}{(\cot 46°19')}$
10–647. $\dfrac{(\sec 10°)(\cot 10°)}{(\sin 10°)(\csc 10°)}$
10–648. $\dfrac{(\sin 35°)(\tan 22°)}{(\sqrt[3]{\sin 5.96°})}$

10–649. $\dfrac{(\sec 11°)(\tan 4°)}{(\cot 49°)}$
10–650. $\dfrac{(\sin 8°)(\tan 9°)}{(\cot 82°)}$
10–651. $\dfrac{(\sin 1.36°)(\cot 26°)}{(\sqrt[3]{0.00916})}$
10–652. $\dfrac{\cot \sin^{-1} 0.916}{(1.32)(5.061)}$
10–653. $\dfrac{(77.19)(\sec 46°)}{(\tan 3.91°)}$

Trigonometric Functions: Problems (continued)

10–654. $\dfrac{(\sqrt[3]{\tan 25.9°})(\sin \cos^{-1} 0.5)}{(\sin 5.16°)(\tan 22°)}$

10–655. $\dfrac{(0.0311)(\sec 69°)\sqrt[3]{9.0}}{(\sin 9°)(\cos 9°)}$

10–656. $\dfrac{(1.916)(\sqrt[3]{1.916})(\sqrt[3]{\sin 20°})}{(\sqrt[3]{\sec 40°})(\tan 10°22')}$

10–657. $\dfrac{(6.17)(\tan 6.17°)(\sqrt[3]{6.17})}{(6.17)^2(\sin 61.7°)(\cos 6.17°)}$

Right Triangle Solution (Log-Log Rule)

In the study of truss design, moments, and free body diagrams, the right triangle plays an important role. Since the Pythagorean theorem is sometimes awkward to use, and mistakes in arithmetic are likely to occur, it is suggested that the following method be used to solve right triangles.

Given: Right triangle with sides a, b, and c and angles A, B, and C (90°), as shown in Figure 10–28.

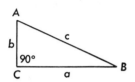

Figure 10–28.

If the smaller side (b) is divided by the longer side (a) and the quotient is greater than 0.100, use *Solution 1*. If the quotient is between 0.100 and 0.0100, use *Solution 2*. If the quotient is less than 0.0100, assume that the hypotenuse (c) is equal in length to the longest side (a) and that angle $B \cong 0°$.

Solution 1

1. Set the index of the T scale above the larger side (a) on the D scale.
2. Move the hairline to the smaller side (b) on the D scale.
3. Read the two angles of the right triangle on the T scale. The larger angle is always opposite the larger side.
4. Move the slide until the smaller of the two angles just read is under the hairline on the sine scale.
5. Read the hypotenuse (c) on the D scale as indicated by the index of the sine scale.

Example:
$$a = 4 \qquad A = ?$$
$$b = 3 \qquad B = ?$$
$$c = ?$$

    a. Set right index of T to 4 on the D scale.
    b. Move the hairline to 3 on the D scale.
    c. Read $B = 36.9°$, $A = 53.1°$ on the T scale. (Note that the smaller angle is opposite the smaller side.)
    d. Move the slide so that 36.9° on the S scale is under the hairline.
    e. Read side $c = 5$ at the right index of the S scale on the D scale.

Solution 2

1. Set the index of the T scale above the largest side (a) on the D scale.
2. Move the hairline to the smaller side (b) on the D scale.
3. Read the smaller angle (B) on the ST scale. The other angle (A) is the complement of B.
4. The hypotenuse is assumed to be equal in length to the largest side.

Solution 3:   This solution is used where the hypotenuse and one side are given.

Example: $a = 5.26$ $A = ?$
                              $b = ?$ $B = ?$
                              $c = 8.75$

a. Set index over 8.75 on D scale.
b. Move hairline to 5.26 on D scale.
c. Read $A = 37.0°$; $B = 53.0°$ on the S scale. (Note that the angle read on the sine scale is opposite the given side.)
d. Set hairline to 37° on the cosine scale.
e. Read $b = 7.0$ on the D scale.

Problems

Solve by right triangle method.

10–658.	$a = 53$ $b = 4$	$B = ?$ $c = ?$		**10–668.**	$a = 11.33$ $B = 26.1°$	$b = ?$ $c = ?$
10–659.	$a = 69.3$ $c = 95$	$b = ?$ $A = ?$		**10–669.**	$a = 0.00197$ $A = 11.36°$	$b = ?$ $c = ?$
10–660.	$a = 37$ $c = 40.3$	$b = ?$ $B = ?$		**10–670.**	$c = 1904$ $A = 18.33°$	$a = ?$ $b = ?$
10–661.	$a = 1.97$ $c = 2.33$	$B = ?$ $b = ?$		**10–671.**	$c = 4.0059$ $B = 86.3°$	$a = ?$ $b = ?$
10–662.	$a = 29.3$ $c = 55.3$	$b = ?$ $A = ?$		**10–672.**	$c = 4.266$ $B = 31.06°$	$a = ?$ $b = ?$
10–663.	$a = 49.3$ $b = 29.6$	$c = ?$ $A = ?$		**10–673.**	$a = 0.00397$ $c = 0.00512$	$b = ?$ $A = ?$
10–664.	$a = 57.3$ $b = 42.1$	$c = ?$ $A = ?$		**10–674.**	$a = 1069$ $A = 85.3°$	$b = ?$ $c = ?$
10–665.	$a = 3.95$ $b = 1.06$	$c = ?$ $B = ?$		**10–675.**	$b = 42.1$ $B = 3.56°$	$a = ?$ $c = ?$
10–666.	$a = 333$ $b = 20$	$A = ?$ $c = ?$		**10–676.**	$a = 0.0317$ $c = 0.0444$	$b = ?$ $B = ?$
10–667.	$a = 591$ $b = 25$	$c = ?$ $B = ?$		**10–677.**	$a = 21.67$ $b = 20.06$	$c = ?$ $B = ?$

The Log-log (Lon) Scales

There are two groups of log-log scales (also called "Lon" scales) on the slide rule. Scales within the two groups are arranged in matched sets. Some slide rules have four matched sets, whereas others have three. These scales are used to obtain the roots, powers, and logarithms of numbers. The matched sets are arranged as follows:

Matched Sets of Log-Log Scales

FOUR SETS		THREE SETS	
For Numbers Larger Than One (called "Lon" scales)	For Numbers Smaller Than One (called "Lon-minus" scales)	(called LL scales)	(called LL_0 scales)
Ln0 . . . . .Ln–0			
Ln1 . . . . .Ln–1		LL_1. . . . . .LL_{01}	
Ln2 . . . . .Ln–2		LL_2. . . . . .LL_{02}	
Ln3 . . . . Ln–3		LL_3. . . . . .LL_{03}	

The C and D scales are used in conjunction with these matched sets of log-log scales. In former years other rules were manufactured with only two LL_0 scales, and these are marked LL_0 and LL_{00}. The A and B scales were used with LL_0 and LL_{00} scales on this type of rule. The general principles discussed below apply to all of the various types of log-log scales.

Scale Construction

If the Lon scales Ln0, Ln1, Ln2, and Ln3 were placed end to end, they would form a continuous scale, as shown in Figure 10–29. Similarly, if the Lon-minus scales Ln-0, Ln-1, Ln-2, Ln-3 were placed end to end, they would form a continuous scale. The Lon-minus scales are graduated from approximately 0.999 to 0.00003 (representing the values of $\epsilon^{-0.001}$ to ϵ^{-10}). The Lon scales are graduated from ap-

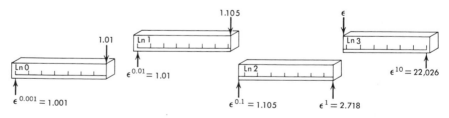

Figure 10–29.

proximately 1.001 to 22,026 (representing the values of $\epsilon^{0.001}$ to ϵ^{10}). Since $\epsilon^0 = 1$, values on both the Lon and Lon-minus scales approach the value 1.0000.

Each division on the Lon and Lon-minus scales represents a single unique number. Thus the decimal point is already marked on these scales for all of the numbers located on the scales. For example, there is only one place on the Lon scales that the number 125.0 may be found. The number 125.0 is found on the Ln3 (LL$_3$) scale, whereas the number 1.25 is found on the Ln2 (LL$_2$) scale. Since the manner in which settings are read on the log-log scales is distinctly different from the method of reading the scales previously studied, the student should be very careful in making his slide rule settings.

Reciprocal Values

The only case where the Lon and Lon-minus (LL and LL$_0$) scales may be used together is in the finding of reciprocals of numbers. The reciprocal of any number on the Lon (LL) scales can be read on the corresponding Lon-minus (LL$_0$) scale.

Examples:

1. Find 1.25 on the Ln2 (LL$_2$) scale. On the Ln-2 (LL$_{02}$) scale its reciprocal can be read as 0.80.
2. Find 236 on the Ln3 (LL$_3$) scale. On the Ln-3 (LL$_{03}$) scale its reciprocal can be read as 0.00424.

Raising a Number to a Power

If such problems as $(5.3)^3 = ?$ were worked entirely by logarithms, the following procedure would be required:

1. $(5.3)^3 = ?$
2. log ans. $= 3(\log 5.3)$
3. log [log ans.] $= \log 3 + \log (\log 5.3)$
4. Answer $= (1.488)(10)^2$

Step 3 is rather involved in many instances. It is for this reason that the log-log scales have been added to the slide rule. Since log-log values of numbers are recorded on the Lon (LL) scales and the log values of numbers have been recorded on the C and D scales, it is quite convenient to perform Step 3 in the preceding example.

The Lon (LL) and Lon–minus (LL$_0$) scales are also used in conjunction with the C and D scales to find powers, roots, and logarithms to the base ϵ of numbers.

In order to raise any number greater than 1.01 to any power:

$$(X)^n = A$$

1. Set the index of the C scale over the value X found on the appropriate Lon (LL) scale (Ln0, Ln1, Ln2, or Ln3).
2. Move the hairline to the value n on the C scale.
3. Read the answer A on the appropriate Lon (LL) scale.

Example:
$$(1.02)^{2.5} = ?$$
$$\log [\log \text{ ans.}] = \log 2.5 + \log (\log 1.02)$$
$$\text{Answer} = 1.0507$$

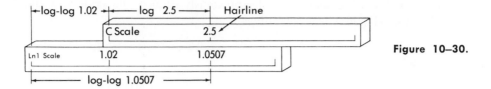

Figure 10–30.

SOLUTION:

1. Set the index of the C scale over the value 1.02 on the Ln1 (LL_1) scale.
2. Move the hairline to the value 2.5 on the C scale.
3. Read the answer 1.0507 on the Ln1 (LL_1) scale.

These scales are arranged so that a number on the Ln3 (LL_3) scale is the tenth power of the number directly below it on the Ln2 (LL_2) scale, and the Ln2 (LL_2) scale gives the tenth power of a number in the corresponding position on the Ln1 (LL_1) scale. Therefore the Ln3 (LL_3) scale would give the one-hundredth power of a number in the corresponding position on the Ln1 (LL_1) scale.

Example:
$$(1.034)^{0.23} = 1.00773 \text{ ans. on the Ln0}$$
$$(1.034)^{2.3} = 1.0799 \text{ ans. on the Ln1 } (LL_1)$$
$$(1.034)^{23.} = 2.156 \text{ ans. on the Ln2 } (LL_2)$$
$$(1.034)^{230.} = 2160 \text{ ans. on the Ln3 } (LL_3)$$

In order to raise any number less than 0.99 to any power:

$$(X)^n = A$$

1. Set the index of the C scale over the value X found on the appropriate Lon–minus (LL_0) scale Ln-0, Ln-1, Ln-2, or Ln-3 (LL_{01}, LL_{02}, or LL_{03}).
2. Move the hairline to the value n on the C scale.
3. Read the answer A on the appropriate Ln–0 (LL_0) scale.

Example: $(0.855)^{4.8} = A$, as shown in Figure 10–31.

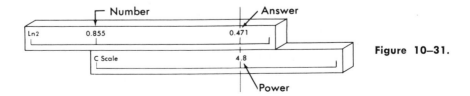

Figure 10–31.

Method of Scale Selection—Powers of Numbers

To use this method, we must consider three factors: (1) the particular log log scale upon which the *number* is located, (2) the power of ten of the exponent when it is expressed in scientific notation, and (3) the particular index of the C scale that is used in the calculation.

1. Each log log scale is given a positive value as follows:

Ln0 = 0	Ln-0 = 0
Ln1 = +1 (Also LL_1)	Ln-1 = +1 (Also LL_{01})
Ln2 = +2 (Also LL_2)	Ln-2 = +2 (Also LL_{02})
Ln3 = +3 (Also LL_3)	Ln-3 = +3 (Also LL_{03})

2. The exponent should be expressed in scientific notation and the power of ten indicated.

3. Assume that the *left* index of the C scale has a value of zero (0) and that the *right* index has a value of plus one (+1).

Rule for Scale Selection of Powers of Numbers

The number of the scale upon which the answer will be read is the algebraic sum of (1) the value of the scale on which the number to be raised is found plus (2) the C scale index value plus (3) the power of ten of the exponent.

Example: $(1.015)^{56} = ?$

Rewrite as $(1.015)^{5.6(10)^1} = ?$

FACTOR	DESCRIPTION OF FACTOR	VALUE	
1.015	1.015 is found on LL_1 scale	+1	
Left Index	Use left index of C scale	0	
56	Power of ten of exponent =1	+1	
?	Sum = Scale location of answer	+2	← Answer on Ln2 (LL_2)

Therefore, the answer will be read under the hairline on the Ln2 (LL_2) scale.

$$(1.015)^{56} = \underline{\underline{2.30}} \qquad \text{Answer}$$

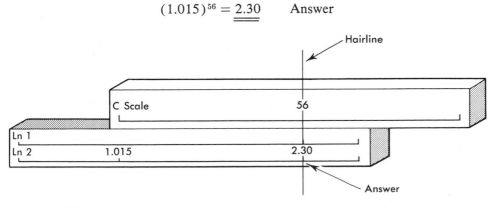

Figure 10–32.

Negative Exponents

In solving problems which involve raising numbers to a negative power, either of two methods may be employed.

Method 1. Set the number and its exponent on the proper scales in the usual manner. Instead of reading the answer on the usual log-log scale, read it on the corresponding scale of the other group.

Example: $$(9.2)^{-3.5} = ?$$

Instead of reading the answer as 2355 on the Ln3 (LL$_3$) scale, read its reciprocal value on the Ln-3 (LL$_{03}$) as 0.000425; therefore

$$(9.2)^{-3.5} = \underline{\underline{4.25 \times 10^{-4}}} \quad \text{(Answer)}$$

Method 2. Set the numbers on the rule in the usual manner, ignoring the negative exponent. When the answer by this operation has been obtained, determine its reciprocal, using the CI scale.

On the slide rules that have only the LL$_0$ and LL$_{00}$ scales, Method 2 is the only method that can be used.

Powers of Numbers: Practice Problems

10–678. $(53.2)^{0.84} = 28.2$

10–679. $(4.65)^{3.68} = 285.$

10–680. $(0.836)^{0.47} = 0.919$

10–681. $(1.0042)^{217} = 2.48$

10–682. $(0.427)^4 = 0.0360$

10–683. $(0.3156)^4 = 0.00988$

10–684. $(0.159)^{0.67} = 0.292$

10–685. $(1.0565)^{49.5} = 15.2$

10–686. $(32.5)^{0.065} = 1.254$

10–687. $(3.45)^{4.65} = 318.$

10–688. $(0.759)^5 = 0.252$

10–689. $(2.127)^4 = 20.5$

10–690. $(2.03)^{-5} = 0.0290$

10–691. $(4.00)^{0.0157} = 1.022$

10–692. $(0.0818)^{-0.777} = 7.00$

10–693. $(1.382)^{21.3} = 980.$

10–694. $(0.071)^{-0.46} = 3.38$

10–695. $(0.232)^{0.0904} = 0.876$

10–696. $(2.718)^{0.405} = 1.50$

10–697. $(0.916)^{0.724} = 0.9384$

10–698. $(1.1106)^{1.72} = 1.197$

10–699. $(59.2)^{-0.43} = 0.1727$

10–700. $(883)^{0.964} = 688.$

10–701. $(7676)^{0.001102} = 1.0099$

10–702. $(4.30)^{0.521} = 2.14$

Finding Roots of Numbers

The process of finding roots of numbers is easier to understand if it is remembered that

$$\sqrt[2.1]{576} = X$$

may be written as $(X)^{2.1} = 576$

Therefore we can "work backward" and apply the principles learned in raising a number to a power. Proceed as follows:

Example:

$$\sqrt[n]{A} = X$$

1. Locate the root n on the C scale to coincide with the value A found on the appropriate log-log scale.
2. Move the hairline to the particular index of the C scale which is located within the body of the rule.
3. Read the answer on the appropriate log log scale.

Example: $\sqrt[3.2]{120} = 4.46$ ans. on Ln3 (LL$_3$), as shown in Figure 10–33.

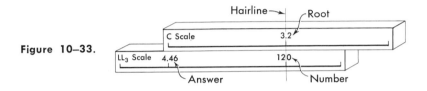

Figure 10–33.

Also $\sqrt[32]{120} = 1.1615$ ans. on Ln2 (LL$_2$)

$\sqrt[320]{120} = 1.0152$ ans. on Ln1 (LL$_1$)

In taking the root of a number, students usually are less certain of the appropriate scale upon which the answer is found. Therefore, a method of scale selection similar to that employed for powers of numbers should be used.

Method of Scale Selection for Roots of Numbers

As before there are three factors which must be considered: (1) the particular log-log scale upon which the *number* is located; (2) the power of ten of the exponent when it is expressed in scientific notation, and (3) the particular index of the C scale which is used in the calculation.

1. Each log-log scale is given a negative value as follows:

Ln0 = 0	Ln-0 = 0
Ln1 = −1 (Also LL$_1$)	Ln-1 = −1 (Also LL$_{01}$)
Ln2 = −2 (Also LL$_2$)	Ln-2 = −2 (Also LL$_{02}$)
Ln3 = −3 (Also LL$_3$)	Ln-3 = −3 (Also LL$_{03}$)

2. The root should be expressed in scientific notation and the power of ten indicated.
3. Assume that the *left* index of the C scale has a value of zero (0) and that the *right* index has a value of plus one (+1).

Rule for Scale Selection for Roots of Numbers

The number of the scale upon which the answer will be read is the algebraic sum of (1) the value of the scale on which the *number whose root is to be determined* is located, plus (2) the C scale index value, plus (3) the power of ten of the root.

Example:

$$\sqrt[4.37]{0.0092} = \text{Answer}$$

FACTOR	DESCRIPTION OF FACTOR	VALUE
0.0092	0.0092 is found on Ln-3 (LL_{03}) Scale	−3
Left Index	Use left index of C scale	0
4.37	Power of ten of root = 0	0
?	Sum = Scale location of Answer	−3	← Answer on Ln-3 (LL_{03})

Therefore, the answer will be read on the Ln-3 (LL_{03}) scale as 0.342.

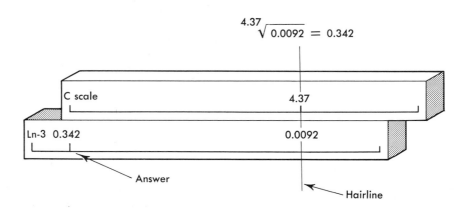

Figure 10–34.

Roots of Numbers Practice Problems

10–703. $\sqrt[7.81]{5.85} = 1.254$

10–704. $\sqrt[6]{0.0835} = 0.661$

10–705. $\sqrt[5]{0.0763} = 0.598$

10–706. $\sqrt[194]{460.} = 1.0321$

10–707. $\sqrt[6]{0.0001} = 0.215$

10–708. $\sqrt[1.65]{8.26} = 3.60$

10–709. $\sqrt[0.34]{0.862} = 0.646$

10–710. $\sqrt[2.3]{85.9} = 6.92$

10–711. $\sqrt[60]{45.} = 1.0655$

10–712. $\sqrt[21.5]{1.606} = 1.0223$

10–713. $\sqrt[1.91]{92.5} = 10.7$

10–714. $\sqrt[50]{0.05} = 0.9418$

10–715. $\sqrt[7]{0.0108} = 0.524$

10–716. $\sqrt[0.006]{0.9762} = 0.018$

10–717. $\sqrt[5.21]{2000} = 4.30$

10–718. $\sqrt[0.04]{0.9792} = 0.592$

10–719. $\sqrt[2.7]{81} = 5.09$

10–720. $\sqrt[2.81]{1.218} = 1.0726$

10–721. $\sqrt[2.15]{52.5} = 6.31$

10–722. $\sqrt[400]{100} = 1.0116$

10–723. $\sqrt[0.75]{2.37} = 3.16$ **10–726.** $\sqrt[5.6]{0.0018} = 0.323$

10–724. $\sqrt[0.073]{1.060} = 2.22$ **10–727.** $\sqrt[0.67]{0.954} = 0.932$

10–725. $\sqrt[1.51]{6.50} = 3.45$

General Guides for Decimal Location

The student should be able to estimate the approximate answer and thereby know on which scale the answer will be found.

The following suggestions are presented so that the student can more easily decide whether the answer is to be larger or smaller than the original quantity.

$$(\text{Number})^{\text{Exponent}} = \text{Answer}$$

1. If the number is larger than 1.00 and the exponent is larger than 1.00, the answer will be greater than the number.

2. If the number is less than 1.00 and the exponent is less than 1.00, the answer will be greater than the number.

3. If the number is less than 1.00 and the exponent is greater than 1.00, the answer will be less than the number.

4. If the number is greater than 1.00 and the exponent is less than 1.00, the answer will be less than the number.

Results That Do Not Fall Within the Limits of the Scales

In many computations the final answer may be larger than 22,026 and hence cannot be read within the limits of the scales. In such cases the original expression must be factored before attempting to use the log–log scales. Several such methods of factoring are explained below.

These methods are for use in finding the powers of numbers. For problems involving roots of numbers convert the problem to one involving the power of a number and then apply the appropriate method.

Example:
$$\sqrt{5} = (5)^{\frac{1}{2}} = (5)^{0.5}$$
$$\sqrt[4]{5} = (5)^{\frac{1}{4}} = (5)^{0.25}$$
$$\sqrt[0.5]{5} = (5)^{\frac{1}{0.5}} = (5)^{2}$$

Method 1. Express the number in scientific notation and raise each part to the given power.

Example:
$$(35.3)^4 = ?$$
$$(35.3)^4 = (3.53 \times 10)^4$$
$$= (3.53)^4 \times (10)^4$$

Now, using the Lon (LL) scales, and since $(3.53)^4 = 155$, we obtain

$$(35.3)^4 = 155. \times 10^4$$
$$= 1.55 \times 10^6 \ (\text{Answer})$$

Method 2. Factor the number which is to be raised to a power and then treat each part separately, as in Method 1.

Example:

$$(15)^5 = ?$$
$$(15)^5 = (3 \times 5)^5$$
$$= (3)^5 \times (5)^5$$
$$= (243)(3125)$$
$$= 7.59 \times 10^5 \quad (\text{Answer})$$

Method 3. Divide the exponent into two or more smaller parts and, using the log-log scales, compute each part separately. A final computation is made using the C and D scales as in Method 1 and Method 2.

Example:

$$(2.36)^{15} = ?$$
$$(2.36)^{15} = (2.36)^5 \times (2.36)^5 \times (2.36)^5$$
$$= (73.2)(73.2)(73.2)$$
$$= 3.93 \times 10^5 \quad (\text{Answer})$$

or

$$(2.36)^{15} = (2.36)^8 \times (2.36)^7$$
$$= (960)(410)$$
$$= 3.93 \times 10^5 \quad (\text{Answer})$$

$$(2.36)^{15} = (2.36)^{7.5} \times (2.36)^{7.5}$$
$$= (620)^2$$
$$= 3.93 \times 10^5 \quad (\text{Answer})$$

Example:

$$(0.000025)^{1.3} = ?$$
$$(0.000025)^{1.3} = (2.5 \times 10^{-5})^{1.3}$$
$$= (2.5)^{1.3} \times (10^{-5})^{1.3}$$
$$= 3.29 \times (10)^{-6.5}$$
$$= (3.29)(10)^{-6}(10)^{-0.5}$$
$$= (3.29)(10)^{-6}\left(\frac{1}{3.16}\right)$$
$$= (3.29)(10)^{-6}(0.316)$$
$$= 1.041 \times 10^{-6} \quad (\text{Answer})$$

Method 4. Express the number in scientific notation and then express the power of 10 in logarithmic form.

Example:

$$(250)^{3.2} = ?$$
$$(250)^{3.2} = (2.50 \times 10^2)^{3.2} = (2.50)^{3.2}(10)^{6.4}$$

where $(10)^{6.4} = x$ may be expressed as $\log_{10} x = 6.4$ or $x = (2.51)(10)^6$

Then
$$(2.50)^{3.2}(10)^{6.4} = (1.87 \times 10^1)(2.51 \times 10^6)$$
and
$$(1.87 \times 10^1)(2.51 \times 10^6) = \underline{\underline{4.71 \times 10^7}}$$

Method 5. This method is more suitable for those numbers which have 5, 6, 7, 8, or 9 as the first digit.

Example:
$$(645)^{13} = ?$$
$$(645)^{13} = (0.645)^{13}(10^3)^{13}$$
$$= (0.00335)(10)^{39}$$
$$= \underline{\underline{3.35(10)^{36}}} \text{ (Answer)}$$

Method 6. Factor the exponent such that one part is equivalent to an exact power of ten.

Example:
$$(2)^{52} = ?$$

First raise the base (2) to a power such that the answer is an exact power of ten.
$$(2)^k = 10{,}000 = (10)^4$$
$$k = 13.29$$

Also:
$$(2)^{52} = (2)^{13.29+13.29+13.29+12.13}$$
$$= (10^4)(10)^4(10)^4(2)^{12.13}$$
$$= (10^4)^3(2)^{12.13}$$
$$= (10)^{12}(4500)$$
$$= \underline{\underline{(4.5)(10)^{15}}} \text{ (Answer)}$$

Example:
$$(1.324)(10)^{-9} = (0.815)^m$$

First choose a factor such that an exact power of ten is obtained.
$$(0.815)^{45} = 0.0001 = (10)^{-4}$$

Then:
$$(1.324)(10)^{-9} = (0.815)^{45+45+t}$$
$$= (0.815)^{45}(0.815)^{45}(0.815)^t$$
$$= (10)^{-4}(10)^{-4}(0.815)^t$$
$$\frac{(1.324)(10)^{-9}}{(10)^{-8}} = (0.815)^t$$
$$1.324(10)^{-1} = (0.815)^t$$
$$t = 9.87$$

Therefore:
$$(1.324)(10)^{-9} = (0.815)^{45+45+9.87}$$
$$(1.324)(10)^{-9} = (0.815)^{99.87}$$

and:
$$m = \underline{\underline{99.9}} \text{ (Answer)}$$

Methods 1 and 6 are generally preferred over the other methods because they usually make greater accuracy possible in the final answer.

Finding the Natural Logarithm of a Number

The natural base for logarithms is $\epsilon(2.71828\text{---})$. The logarithm of any number (to the base ϵ) may be found as follows:

For Numbers Greater than 1.00
$$\log_\epsilon X = A$$

1. Locate the number X on the Ln0, Ln1 (LL_1), Ln2 (LL_2), or Ln3 (LL_3) scale.
2. Read the logarithm of the number under the hairline on the D scale.

Location of Decimal Point

If the number X is on	Decimal point in the answer
Ln3 or LL_3	x.xxx
Ln2 or LL_2	0.xxx
Ln1 or LL_1	0.0xxx
Ln0	0.00xx

Examples:
$$\log_\epsilon 62 \ = 4.13$$
$$\log_\epsilon 1.271 = 0.240$$
$$\log_\epsilon 1.026 = 0.0257$$

For numbers Less than 1.00

$$\log_\epsilon X = A$$

1. Locate the number X on the Ln–0, Ln–1 (LL_{01}), Ln–2 (LL_{02}), or Ln–3 (LL_{03}) scales.
2. Read the logarithm (to the base ϵ) of the number A directly above X on the D scale.

Location of Decimal Point

If the number X is on	Decimal point in the answer
Ln-3 or LL_{03}	–x.xxx
Ln-2 or LL_{02}	–0.xxx
Ln-1 or LL_{01}	–0.0xxx
Ln-0	–0.00xx

3. The logarithm (to the base ϵ) of all numbers less than 1.000 is a negative number.

Examples:
$$\log_\epsilon 0.0045 = -5.40$$
$$\log_\epsilon 0.745 \ = -0.294$$
$$\log_\epsilon 0.954 \ = -0.0471$$

Problems

Solve, using the log–log scales.

10–728. $(2.89)^6$

10–729. $(4.11)^{5.2}$

10–730. $(19.01)^{1.6}$

10–731. $(1.185)^{2.7}$

10–732. $(1.033)^{5.8}$

10–733. $(1.0134)^{25}$

10–734. $(3.95)^{0.65}$

10–735. $(8.46)^{0.134}$

10–736. $(81.2)^{0.118}$

10–737. $(7850.)^{0.0775}$

10–738. $(1.399)^{0.883}$

10–739. $(10.06)^{0.0621}$

10–740. $(0.569)^4$

10–741. $(0.157)^8$

10–742. $(0.985)^{1.568}$

10–743. $(0.318)^{4.65}$

10–744. $(0.078)^{0.458}$

10–745. $(17.91)^{0.012}$

10–746. $(4780.)^{0.913}$

10–747. $(253.)^{0.269}$

10–748. $(0.428)^{0.559}$

10–749. $(4.08)^{24}$

10–750. $(3.91)^{20}$

10–751. $(8.45)^{16}$

10–752. $(7.77)^{42}$

10–753. $(16.89)^{1.402}$

10–754. $(87.8)^8$

10–755. $(0.1164)^{0.33}$

10–756. $(0.779)^{0.43}$

10–757. $(867.)^6$

10–758. $(91.05)^{14}$

10–759. $(0.775)^{0.0259}$

10–760. $\sqrt[6]{8.69}$

10–761. $\sqrt[5]{1.094}$

10–762. $\sqrt[1.3]{8.74}$

10–763. $\sqrt[0.6]{19.77}$

10–764. $\sqrt[18]{54.8}$

10–765. $\sqrt[7]{1.004}$

10–766. $\sqrt[1.95]{0.642}$

10–767. $\sqrt[14]{0.1438}$

10–768. $\sqrt[3.6]{0.952}$

10–769. $\sqrt[2.4]{0.469}$

10–770. $\sqrt[1.7]{0.1975}$

10–771. $\sqrt[0.55]{0.2218}$

10–772. $\sqrt[0.46]{16,430.}$

10–773. $\sqrt[0.133]{507.}$

10–774. $\sqrt[0.57]{0.964}$

10–775. $\sqrt[5.09]{6.49}$

10–776. $\sqrt[13.6]{0.1574}$

10–777. $\sqrt[2.09]{0.1268}$

Solve for X

10–778. $X = (43.8)^{6.4}$

10–779. $X = (1.853)^{0.447}$

10–780. $(31.77)^x = 1.164$

10–781. $(2.388)^{3x} = 3.066$

10–782. $(1.064)^{0.2x} = 4.99$

10–783. $(X)^{5.8} = 8.57$

10–784. $(4.92)^{0.66x} = 24.1$

10–785. $(0.899)^{4.7x} = (1.552)(10)^{-8}$

10–786. $(0.1135)^{0.77x} = 0.775$

10–787. $(11.774)^{8.31x} = 12.88$

10–788. $(18.73)^{6.4x} = 8688.$

10–789. $(34.86)^{1.117x} = 9.44$

10–790. $(0.631)^{0.64x} = 0.318$

10–791. $(0.1299)^{0.68x} = 0.443$

10–792. $(15.84)^x = 4.87$

10–793. $(0.679)^x = 0.337$

10–794. $(1.461)^{19.66x} = 9.07$

10–795. $(0.766)^{5.8x} = 0.239$

10–796. $(X)^{7.99} = 0.775$

10–797. $(X)^{0.175} = 8.53$

10–798. $(X)^{3.33} = 1.055$

10–799. $(X)^{0.871} = 0.1557$

10–800. $(X)^{4.77} = 1.088$

10–801. $(X)^{0.771} = 0.0521$

10–802. $(4.51)^{0.199} = \dfrac{X}{3}$

Solve for the natural logarithms of the following numbers:

10–803. 15.77

10–804. 19,850.

10–805. 0.7789

10–806. 0.1845

10–807. 1.896

10–808. 56.87

10–809. 13.09

10–810. 33.4

10–811. 8.09

10–812. 1.571

10–813. 0.1345

10–814. 0.915

10–815. 0.001233

10–816. 13,890.

10–817. 2.066

10–818. 1.3157

10–819. 1.0047

10–820. 89.78

10–821. 0.664

10–822. 0.459

10–823. 0.1175

10–824. 1.9974

10–825. 0.9974

10–826. 0.2378

10–827. 0.01663

Review Problems

Solve by general slide rule methods.

10–828. $(51)(9)$

10–829. $(426)(51)$

10–830. $(6.03)(5.16)$

10–831. $(561)(4956)$

10–832. $(43.2)(0.617)$

10–833. $(6617)(0.00155)$

10–834. $(99.043)(3.091)$

10–835. $(0.0617)(0.4417)$

10–836. $(1.035)(2.31 \times 10^5)$

10–837. $(79.81 \times 10^{-4})(0.617)$

10–838. $(516 \times 10^{-8})(0.391 \times 10^{-2})$

10–839. $(51)(97)(32)$

10–840. $(52.3)(759.3)$

10–841. $(716.5)(0.03166)$

10–842. $(11.65)(-0.9213)$

10–843. $(76.2)(-31.45)$

10–844. $(-0.6175)(-12,391)$

10–845. $\dfrac{(-759.6)}{(0.6175)}$

10–846. $\dfrac{(-19.96)}{(3346)}$

10–847. $\dfrac{(-1.0366)}{(29.31)}$

10–848. $\dfrac{(7575)}{(695.2)}$

10–849. $\dfrac{(-516.6)}{(0.06052)}$

10–850. $(116.5)(4619)(0.317)$

10–851. $(210.9)(151.3)(7716)$

10–852. $(706.5)(1.695 \times 10^{-6})(0.006695)$

10–853. $(1033)(7.339 \times 10^{-6})(0.0317 \times 10^{-3})$

10–854. $(4.017 \times 10^{-8})(0.0991)(0.1756)$

10–855. $(5.576)(0.0917)(1.669 \times 10^4)$

10–856. $(6.991)(0.75)(0.993)(4.217)$

10–857. $(56.88)(0.971 \times 10^{-5})$

10–858. $(59.17)(0.3617)(0.5916)(0.00552)$

10–859. $(5.691)(0.3316)(0.991)(0.00554)(0.1712)$

10–860. $(6.523)(71.22)(4.091)(591)(600)(0.1332)$

10–861. $(43.06)(0.2361)(0.905 \times 10^{-4})(3.617 \times 10^{-3})$

10–862. $(1917)^{2.16}$

10–863. $(4.216)^{1.517}$

10–864. $(2.571)^{2.91}$

10–865. $(0.3177)^{2.06}$

10–866. $\sqrt[5]{26.31}$

10–867. $\sqrt[3]{0.03175}$

10–868. $\sqrt{116.75}$

10–869. $\sqrt[3]{0.6177}$

10–870. $\sqrt{3167}$

10–871. $(179 \times 10^3)(0.3165)$

10–872. $(5033 \times 10^{-4})(0.9116)$

10–873. $(0.06105)(77.165)$

10–874. $(\sqrt{216})(34)(\pi)^2$

10–875. $(\sqrt{819})(107)(\sqrt{\pi})$

10–876. $\dfrac{(\sqrt{616})\,(6.767)}{(\sqrt{39.6})}$

10–877. $\dfrac{(1045)}{(X)} = \dfrac{(0.0278)}{(0.0798)}$

10–878. $\dfrac{(1.486)}{(33)} = \dfrac{(0.37)\,(X)}{467}$

10–879. $(816) = \dfrac{(244)\,(2\pi)}{(0.049)\,(X)}$

10–880. $(0.0036)\,(\sin 49.8°)$

10–881. $\dfrac{(20.5)^2(7.49)\,(\sin 49°)}{(30.5)\,(0.0987)}$

10–882. $\sqrt{\dfrac{(38)^2(6.71)^2}{\pi}}$

10–883. $(7.61)\,(\sqrt[3]{7.61})\,(\pi)$

10–884. $\dfrac{(13.1)\,(\sin 3.12°)}{(\tan 41.9°)}$

10–885. $\dfrac{2}{3} = \dfrac{(X)\,(\pi)}{8.37}$

10–886. $\dfrac{(9616)}{X} = \dfrac{(3.1416)}{(0.0142)}$

10–887. $(\sqrt[3]{64.9})\,(2.1 \times 10^3)$

10–888. $(4 \times 10^6)\,(0.007) = (X)\,(10{,}980)$

10–889. $Y = \left(\dfrac{1}{4}\right)\left(\dfrac{16}{6}\right)\left(\dfrac{1}{17}\right)$

10–890. $\dfrac{X}{\pi} = \dfrac{(\sqrt{46.2})\,(3.14)^2}{(\sin 3.7°)}$

10–891. $\dfrac{(3.98)\,(X)}{(1.07)\,(38)} = \dfrac{(3 \times 10^6)}{(17{,}680)}$

10–892. $\dfrac{(\sqrt[3]{986})}{X} = \dfrac{(14)}{(1/116)}$

10–893. $\dfrac{(X)^2}{(9.2)} = \dfrac{(18.17)\,(3.4)}{(166)}$

10–894. $\dfrac{(3.6)}{(X)^2} = \dfrac{(9.6 \times 10^2)}{(67.4)} = \dfrac{(Y)^{\frac{1}{2}}}{(64)}$

10–895. $\dfrac{(X)^{\frac{1}{2}}}{(31.1)} = \dfrac{(\sqrt{196})\,(189.1)}{4/76}$

10–896. $\dfrac{(96.5)}{(3.9)} = \dfrac{X}{(\sin 46.6°)} = \dfrac{(Y)^2}{(3.14 \times 10^{-2})}$

10–897. $\dfrac{(X)^2}{Y} = \dfrac{(67.3)^2(Y)}{(96.61)} = \dfrac{(497.1)}{\tan 75°}$

10–898. $\dfrac{(3.7)\,(4.9)}{X} = \dfrac{(46.7)}{564}$

Review Problems (continued)

Solve by general slide rule methods:

10–899. $\dfrac{Y}{(28)} = \dfrac{(3.2)}{(4/118)}$

10–900. $\dfrac{Y}{42} = \dfrac{39.1}{(1/45)}$

10–901. $(37.3)(X)(46.6) = (175)(\pi)$

10–902. $(\sqrt{256})(3) = (X)(197.6)$

10–903. $\dfrac{(54.6)(\tan 10.6°)}{(\sqrt{0.0967})(8.1 \times 10^3)}$

10–904. $\dfrac{\sqrt[3]{(15.1)^2(31.4)^2}}{(\sin \text{ arc } \cos 0.617)}$

10–905. $\dfrac{(0.954)(0.06 \times 10^3)}{(\tan 59°)^{1/2}(6.5)^2}$

10–906. $\dfrac{\sqrt[3]{(15.6)^2}(0.9618)}{(0.08173)(61,508)(2\pi)}$

10–907. $\dfrac{(68)(765)(391)(0.0093 \times 10^3)}{(571)^2(\sqrt[3]{(64)})}$

10–908. $\dfrac{(\cos 11.5°)(\sqrt{6.87})}{(0.00081)(7.7 \times 10^4)}$

10–909. $\dfrac{\sqrt[4]{(1.71)^5}(6.87)}{(\tan 53°)(5.1)^2}$

10–910. $\dfrac{(0.000817)(\tan 81°)}{(0.00763)(\tan 81°)}$

10–911. $(273)^{\frac{1}{2}}(46.9)(\cos 61°)(\pi^3)$

10–912. $\dfrac{(\sin \text{ arc } \tan 3.17)(71.7)}{(\sqrt{89.6})(\sqrt[4]{(76.5)^2})}$

10–913. $\dfrac{(\sqrt{(16)^3})(\log_{10} 100)}{(6.71 \times 10^{-1})(3.71)^3}$

10–914. $\dfrac{(6.93)(\sin \cos^{-1} 0.98)}{(0.937)^2(39.6)}$

10–915. $\dfrac{(\sqrt{91.68})(\sqrt[3]{65.9})}{(\tan 68.7°)(0.671)^2}$

10–916. $\dfrac{(4.5)^4(\sqrt{(98.71)})(\sin 56.4°)}{(0.09 \times 10)(38.6)^{3/2}}$

10–917. $\dfrac{(\sqrt{285})(\cos 36.6°)(1.64)^2}{(67.1 \times 10^{-1})(5780)}$

10–918. $\dfrac{(\tan \sin^{-1} 0.87)(61.7)}{(5.64)^{0.98}(3.65)^2}$

10–919. $\dfrac{(3174)(\tan 64°)}{(81.6)^2(\sqrt[3]{18})}$

10–920. $\dfrac{(44.6)(0.09 \times 10^3)(\sin 80.9°)}{(\sqrt[3]{96.7})(51.6)^2}$

10–921. $\dfrac{(\tan 50.6°)(3.4)^2}{(\sqrt{9681})(171)}$

10–922. $\dfrac{(296)(0.197 \times 10^5)}{\sqrt[4]{(76.1)}(\sin 49.6°)}$

10–923. $\dfrac{(\sin 22.6°)(9.918)}{(\tan 31.6°)(98.71)}$

10–924. $\dfrac{(68.7 \times 10^2)(\tan 56.1°)}{(96.7)^{0.86}(18,614)}$

10–925. $\dfrac{(0.0098)(\sin 17.6°)\sqrt{(0.186)}}{(41.6)^2(689.0)}$

10–926. $\dfrac{(\tan 19.8°)^2(6.71 \times 10^3)}{(1,876)(\sqrt[4]{59})}$

10–927. $\dfrac{(\sqrt{\sin 40°})(17)^2(4\pi^2)}{(0.643)(\tan 60°)}$

Hyperbolic Functions on the Slide Rule

Hyperbolic functions are useful in several mathematical applications such as the variation of electrical current and voltage with distance in the calculation of transmission of electrical power. Several manufacturers of slide rules make special scales from which hyperbolic functions can be read directly. However, it is possible to obtain numerical values for hyperbolic functions using conventional scales by making use of the relations:

$$\frac{\epsilon^x - \epsilon^{-x}}{2} = \text{hyperbolic sine } x \text{ (sinh } x\text{)}$$

$$\frac{\epsilon^x + \epsilon^{-x}}{2} = \text{hyperbolic cosine } x \text{ (cosh } x\text{)}$$

$$\frac{\epsilon^{2x} - 1}{\epsilon^{2x} + 1} = \text{hyperbolic tangent } x \text{ (tanh } x\text{)}$$

Reading Hyperbolic Scales

Most slide rules that have hyperbolic scales have the scales marked as Sh and Th. Slide rules manufactured by Pickett identify the hyperbolic sine scales as *upper* and *lower* and the values of sinh x are read on the C scale. Keuffel & Esser identify the hyperbolic sine scales as Sh 1 and Sh 2 and values of sinh x are read on the D scale. Except for these minor differences, reading hyperbolic functions on slide rules made by either company is essentially the same.

Hyperbolic Sines. In order to read hyperbolic sine functions on the slide rule, set the value sinh x on one of the Sh scales and read the value of the function on either the C scale or the D scale under the hairline.

Example: Find sinh 0.38

SOLUTION: Locate 0.38 on the upper Sh scale or on the Sh 1 scale and read 0.389 on the C or D scale.

Example: Find sinh 1.88

SOLUTION: Using the method above read sinh $1.88 = 3.20$. Note that the value 1.88 is located on the lower Sh scale (Sh 2 scale) and 3.20 is read on the C scale (D scale).

The decimal point can be determined readily by noting that numbers corresponding to function values on the upper Sh (Sh 1) scale lie between 0.1 and 1.0, and numbers corresponding to function values on the lower Sh (Sh 2) scale lie between 1.0 and 10.0.

Hyperbolic Tangents. Hyperbolic tangents can be read by locating the value of the tangent function on the Th scale and reading the number on the C or D scale under the hairline.

Example: tanh $0.206 = 0.1990$

Example: tanh $1.33 = 0.870$

Hyperbolic Cosines. Most slide rules do not have a hyperbolic cosine scale. Values for the hyperbolic cosine can be determined by use of the relation:

$$\cosh x = \frac{\sinh x}{\tanh x}$$

In finding values for cosh x using the Pickett rule, first set the slide so the indexes coincide. Locate the hairline over the value of x on the appropriate Sh scale. Move the slide until the value of x on the Th scale is under the hairline and cosh x can be read on the D scale at the C index.

Example: cosh $0.482 = 1.118$

Example: cosh $1.08 = 1.642$

For the Keuffel & Esser Vector slide rule, this procedure can be followed. Set an index of the slide on the value of x on the Th scale. Set the hairline on the value of x on either Sh 1 or Sh 2, depending on its amount. Read the value of cosh x on the C scale.

Example: cosh $0.305 = 1.046$

Example: cosh $1.81 = 2.31$

When the value of cosh x is given and it is desired to find x, use can be made of the relation

$$\cosh^2 x - \sinh^2 x = 1$$

Example: Find the value of x when $\cosh x = 2.1$

SOLUTION:

$$\sinh x = \sqrt{\cosh^2 x - 1}$$

Substituting:

$$\sinh x = \sqrt{(2.1)^2 - 1}$$
$$\sinh x = \sqrt{3.41}$$

and

$$\sinh x = 1.85$$

Set 1.85 on the C (D) scale and read the value of x on the lower Sh (Sh 2) scale. The lower scale is used because $\sinh x$ is greater than 1.

Then

$$x = 1.372$$

Approximations for Large and Small Values of x

When the value of x is more than 3, it can be shown that the value of $\sinh x$ and $\cosh x$ is approximately the same as $\dfrac{\epsilon^x}{2}$.

Example:

$$\sinh 4.2 = ?$$

$$\frac{\epsilon^{4.2}}{2} = 33.5$$

$$\sinh 4.2 \cong 33.5$$

Also for large values of x, $\tanh x$ is approximately 1.0.

Example:

$$\tanh 3.7 = ?$$

SOLUTION:

$$\tanh 3.7 = \frac{\epsilon^{(2)(3.7)} - 1}{\epsilon^{(2)(3.7)} + 1}$$

$$= \frac{1650 - 1}{1650 + 1}$$

$$\tanh 3.7 \cong 1.0$$

When x has values below 0.1, it can be shown that $\sinh x$ and $\tanh x$ are approximately the same as x, and $\cosh x$ is approximately 1.0.

Example:

$$\sinh 0.052 \cong 0.052$$
$$\tanh 0.037 \cong 0.037$$
$$\cosh 0.028 \cong 1.00$$

Other Hyperbolic Functions.   While not often needed, other hyperbolic functions can be obtained by using the following defining expressions:

$$\coth x = \frac{1}{\tanh x}$$

$$\text{sech } x = \frac{1}{\cosh x}$$

$$\text{csch } x = \frac{1}{\sinh x}$$

Problems on Hyperbolic Functions

10–928. Find the values of sinh x for the following values of x: (*a*) 0.12, (*b*) 1.07, (*c*) 1.91, (*d*) 2.30, (*e*) 3.11, (*f*) 4.26, (*g*) 5.00

10–929. Find the values of x for the following values of sinh x: (*a*) 0.1304, (*b*) 0.956, (*c*) 1.62, (*d*) 4.10, (*e*) 8.70, (*f*) 19.42, (*g*) 41.96

10–930. Find the values of cosh x for the following values of x: (*a*) 0.28, (*b*) 1.03, (*c*) 1.98, (*d*) 2.37, (*e*) 3.56, (*f*) 4.04, (*g*) 5.00

10–931. Find the values of x for the following values of cosh x: (*a*) 1.024, (*b*) 1.374, (*c*) 2.31, (*d*) 5.29, (*e*) 8.50, (*f*) 21.7, (*g*) 52.3

10–932. Find the values of tanh x for the following values of x: (*a*) 0.16, (*b*) 0.55, (*c*) 1.14, (*d*) 1.94, (*e*) 2.34, (*f*) 2.74, (*g*) 5.00

10–933. Find the values of x corresponding to the following values of tanh x: (*a*) 0.1781, (*b*) 0.354, (*c*) 0.585, (*d*) 0.811, (*e*) 0.881, (*f*) 0.980, (*g*) 0.990

Slide Rule Solution of Complex Numbers

A complex number, which consists of a real part and an imaginary part, is often used to describe a vector quantity. By definition, a vector quantity, frequently referred to as a *phasor* in electrical engineering, has both magnitude and direction. For example, the expression $3 + j4$ will describe a vector which is $\sqrt{3^2 + 4^2}$ units long and makes an angle arc tan $\frac{4}{3}$ with an x-axis. For a more complete discussion on complex number theory, refer to a text on basic algebra.

The symbol i or the symbol j is customarily used to represent the quantity $\sqrt{-1}$. In the discussion in this section the symbol $j = \sqrt{-1}$ will be used.

If we let the scalar length of a vector be designated as R, as shown in Figure 10–35, then we can write $R\epsilon^{j\theta} = x + jy$ in polar form as $R\underline{/\theta}$. This expression $R\underline{/\theta}$ is a shortened form of $R\epsilon^{j\theta}$ which is obtained from the identity

$$R\epsilon^{j\theta} = R \cos\theta + jR \sin\theta.$$

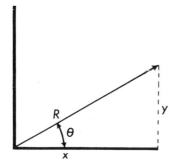

Figure 10–35.

Complex Numbers on the Slide Rule. From trigonometric relations for a right triangle, we can show that tan $\theta = \frac{y}{x}$; $R = \frac{y}{\sin\theta}$; and $R = \frac{x}{\cos\theta}$. We can use these relations to solve complex number problems on the slide rule. Take, for example, the complex number $3 + j4$ and let it be required to find R/θ.

The following method will give the solution to this problem on most types of slide rules:

1. Locate the larger of the two numbers on the D scale and set an index of the C scale at this number. Locate the smaller of the two numbers on the D scale using the hairline, and read the angle θ on the T scale under the hairline. If y is smaller than x, θ is less than 45°, and if y is larger than x, θ is larger than 45°.

2. Next move the slide until the angle θ on the S scale is in line with the smaller of the two numbers. Read R on the D scale at the index of the C scale.

Example: Express $3 + j4$ in polar form

SOLUTION: Set the right index of the C scale at 4 on the D scale.

Move the hairline to 3 on the D scale and read $\theta = 53.1°$ on the T scale. Note that the y value is larger than the x value; thus the angle is larger than 45°.

Without moving the hairline, move the slide until 53.1° on the S scale (reading angles to the left) is under the hairline.

Read 5 at the right index of the C scale.

The solution is $3 + j4 = 5/53.1°$

This method can be performed on most types of rules, requiring the minimum number of manipulations of the rule. It also can be applied readily to the solution of most problems involving right triangles.

When any of the complex numbers have a minus sign, the slide rule operation to solve the problem is the same as though the sign of the numbers were positive. The angles usually are determined by inspection using trigonometric relations. The following general rules apply:

If the expression has the form $+x + jy$, θ is in the first quadrant.

For $-x + jy$, θ is in the second quadrant
For $-x - jy$, θ is in the third quadrant
For $+x - jy$, θ is in the fourth quadrant

Example: Express $-7.1 + j3.8$ in polar form.

SOLUTION: Set the right index of the C scale at 7.1 on the D scale, and read on the T scale $\theta = 28.3°$ at 3.8 on the D scale.

Move the slide so that 28.3° on the S scale is over 3.8 and read $R = 8.03$ at the C index.

By inspection, the angle is in the second quadrant and the total angle is $180° - 28.3° = 151.7°$.

Therefore, the polar form is $8.03/151.7°$.

Example: Express $4 - j3$ in polar form.

SOLUTION: The angle is read as 36.9° and is in the fourth quadrant. The total angle is $360° - 36.9° = 323.1°$.

The polar form is $5/323.1°$.

If the polar form is given, the rectangular form can be obtained by multiplying the value of R by the appropriate sine and cosine value. A rapid method of finding the quantities is to use the previously described slide rule manipulation in reverse.

Example: Express $3.3/28°$ in rectangular form.

SOLUTION: Set the right index of the C scale at 3.3 on the D scale and read 1.55 on D under 28° on the sine scale.

Move the slide until 28° on the T scale is over 1.55 on the D scale.

Read 2.915 on the D scale at the right index. Since the angle is less than 45°, the imaginary part of the complex number is the smaller of the two. Therefore,

$$3.3/28° = 2.915 + j1.55$$

If the polar angle is larger than 45°, angles on the T scale and S scale are read to the left, and the real part of the complex number is read first. The real part of the number will be the smaller of the two parts.

Example: $$179/66° = 72.9 + j163.5$$

For angles not in the first quadrant, obtain the angle of the vector with respect to the x-axis and treat the solution as outlined above. By inspection, affix the proper signs to the real and imaginary parts after obtaining their values. A sketch will help greatly in this process.

Conversion for Small Angles. If the ratio of the x value and y value in the complex number is greater than 10, the angle can be found on the ST scale. The real value is approximately equal to the value of R.

Example: $$35 + j1.5 = R/\theta$$

SOLUTION: Set the C index at 35 on the D scale and read $\theta = 2.45°$ on the ST scale.

Then $R/\theta \cong 35/2.45°$.

Example: $$0.075/4.1° = x + jy$$

SOLUTION: Set the C index at 0.075 on the D scale. Read 0.00536 on D under 4.1° on ST.

Then $x + jy \cong 0.075 + j0.00536$.

Conversion for Angles Near 90°. For angles between 84.27° and 90°, the ratio of x to y will be 10 or greater and the imaginary part of the complex number is approximately equal to the value of R. The angle can be read on the ST scale after subtracting it from 90°.

Example:
$$18/\underline{88°} = x + jy$$

SOLUTION: Set the left index of C at 18 on the D scale. Read 0.6 on D under 2° on the ST scale.

Then $x + jy \cong 0.6 + j18$.

Remember that for very large and very small angles, the ratio of x and y will be 10 or greater, and either the real part or the imaginary part of the complex number will be approximately equal to the value of R.

Applications of Complex Numbers. In solving problems involving complex numbers, addition and subtraction of complex numbers are more easily performed if the numbers are expressed in rectangular form. In this form, the respective real parts and imaginary parts can be added or subtracted directly. However, to multiply or divide complex numbers, it is more convenient to express them in polar form and solve by multiplying or dividing the vector magnitude, and adding or subtracting the angular magnitude.

Examples:

$$(a + jb) + (c + jd) = (a + c) + j(b + d) \text{ (Addition)}$$
$$(a + jb) - (c + jd) = (a - c) + j(b - d) \text{ (Subtraction)}$$
$$(a/\underline{\theta_1})(b/\underline{\theta_2}) = (a)(b)/\underline{\theta_1 + \theta_2} \quad \text{(Multiplication)}$$

$$\frac{a/\underline{\theta_1}}{b/\underline{\theta_2}} = \frac{a}{b}/\underline{\theta_1 - \theta_2} \qquad \text{(Division)}$$

From the examples above, we can see that the ability to perform rapid conversions from polar form to rectangular form or vice versa will be helpful in solving problems involving complex numbers.

Problems on Complex Numbers

10–934. Express in polar form: (*a*) $8 + j3$, (*b*) $2 + j6$, (*c*) $1 + j4$, (*d*) $5 + j5$

10–935. Express in rectangular form: (*a*) $6.2/\underline{39°}$, (*b*) $3.6/\underline{48°}$, (*c*) $9.2/\underline{21.4°}$, (*d*) $2.7/\underline{71°}$

10–936. Express in polar form: (*a*) $-8.9 + j4.2$, (*b*) $-16.8 + j9.3$, (*c*) $-5.3 + j2.1$, (*d*) $-18.4 + j3.3$

10–937. Express in rectangular form: (*a*) $9.7/\underline{118°}$, (*b*) $115/\underline{137°}$, (*c*) $2.09/\underline{160°}$, (*d*) $5.72/\underline{110°}$

10–938. Express in polar form: (*a*) $-7.3 - j6.1$, (*b*) $-4.4 - j8.2$, (*c*) $-8.8 - j2.5$, (*d*) $-1.053 - j5.13$

10–939. Express in rectangular form: (*a*) $81.3/\underline{200°}$, (*b*) $62.1/\underline{253°}$, (*c*) $1059/\underline{197°}$, (*d*) $0.912/\underline{231°}$

Problems on Complex Numbers (continued)

10–940. Express in polar form: (a) $160.5 - j147$, (b) $89.3 - j46.2$, (c) $0.0062 - j0.0051$, (d) $3.07 - j1.954$

10–941. Express in rectangular form: (a) $557\underline{/297°}$, (b) $6.03\underline{/327°}$, (c) $0.9772\underline{/344°}$, (d) $19,750\underline{/300°}$

10–942. Express in polar form: (a) $15.61 + j7.09$, (b) $-14.9 - j61.7$, (c) $0.617 - j0.992$, (d) $-41.2 + j75.3$

10–943. Express in rectangular form: (a) $1.075\underline{/29.1°}$, (b) $10.75\underline{/136°}$, (c) $107.5\underline{/253°}$, (d) $1075\underline{/322°}$

Part Two

The Engineering Method
of Problem Solving

The engineer is known for his problem solving ability. It is probably this ability more than any other that has enabled many engineers to rise to positions of leadership and top management within their companies.

In problem solving, both in school and in industry, considerable importance is attached to a proper analysis of the problem, to a logical recording of the problem solution, and to the overall professional appearance of the finished calculations. Neatness and clarity of presentation are distinguishing marks of the engineer's work. Students should strive always to practice professional habits of problem analysis and to make a conscious effort to improve the appearance of each paper, whether it is submitted for grading or is included in a notebook.

The computation paper used for most calculations is 8½ by 11 inches in size, with lines ruled both vertically and horizontally on the sheet. Usually these lines divide the paper into five squares per inch, and the paper is commonly known as cross-section paper or engineering calculation paper. Many schools use paper that has the lines ruled on the reverse side of the paper so that erasures will not remove them. A fundamental principle to be followed is that the problem work shown on the paper should not be crowded, and all steps of the solution should be included.

Engineers use slant or vertical lettering (see Figure 11–1), and either is acceptable as long as there is no mixing of the two forms. The student should not be discouraged if he finds that he cannot letter with great speed and dexterity at first. Skills in making good letters improve with hours of patient practice. Use a well-sharpened H or 2H pencil and follow the sequence of strokes recommended in Figure 11–1.

Several styles of model problem sheets are shown in Figures 11–2 and 11–3. Notice in each sample that an orderly sequence is followed in which the known data are given first. The data are followed by a brief statement of the requirements, and then the engineer's solution.

When the problem solution is finished, the paper may be folded and endorsed on the outside or may be submitted flat in a folder. Items that appear on the

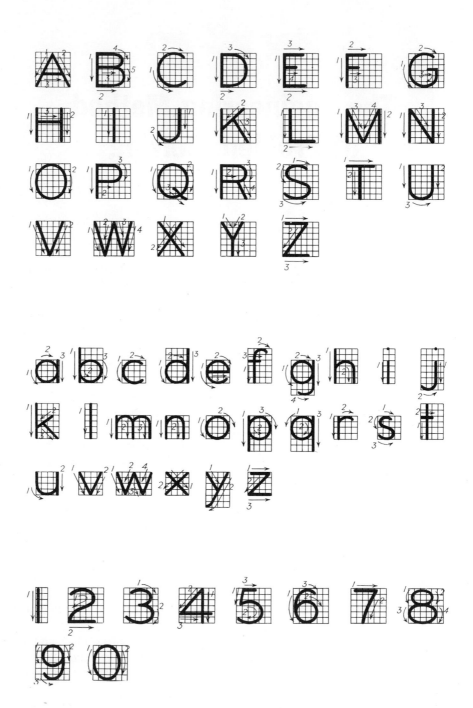

Figure 11–1. Vertical lettering.

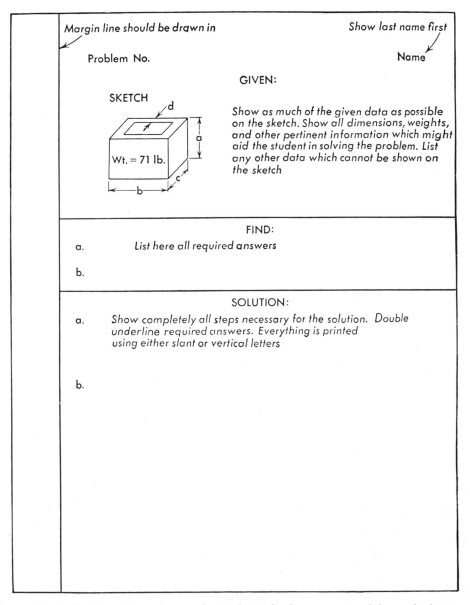

Margin line should be drawn in

Show last name first

Problem No.

Name

GIVEN:

SKETCH

Wt. = 71 lb.

Show as much of the given data as possible on the sketch. Show all dimensions, weights, and other pertinent information which might aid the student in solving the problem. List any other data which cannot be shown on the sketch

FIND:

a. List here all required answers

b.

SOLUTION:

a. Show completely all steps necessary for the solution. Double underline required answers. Everything is printed using either slant or vertical letters

b.

Figure 11–2. Model problem sheet, style A. This style shows a general form which is useful in presenting the solution of mensuration problems.

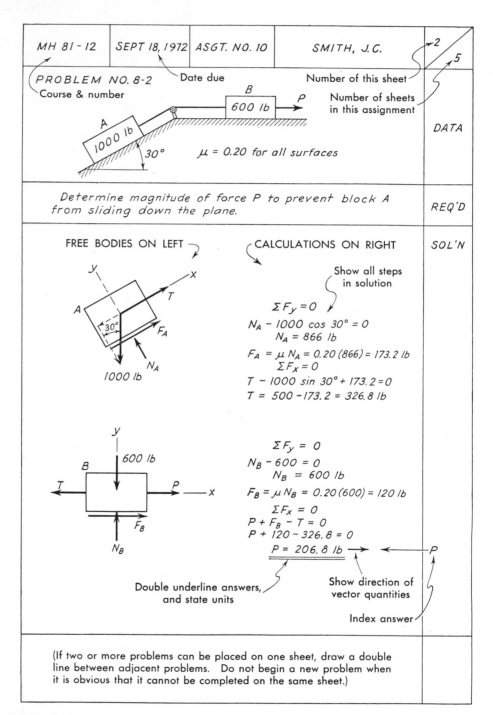

Figure 11–3. Model problem sheet, style B. This style shows a method of presenting stated problems. Notice that all calculations are shown on the sheet and that no scratch calculations on other sheets are used.

endorsement should include the student's name, and the course, section, date, problem numbers, and any other prescribed information.

Problem solving may be considered in some degree to be both *art* and *science*. The *art* of problem solving is developed over a period of continuous practice, whereas the *science* of problem solving comes about through a study of the engineering method of problem solving. Both engineers and scientists must be "problem solvers." However, in many instances the end product of the engineer's analysis, which is a working system economically devised, is considerably different from that of the scientist's, which may be a solution without regard to economics or usefulness. Before analyzing the "engineering method," let us consider the two types of thought processes used by the engineer in his problem solving.

TYPES OF THOUGHT PROCESSES

Deductive Reasoning

The laws of reasoning by deduction, sometimes called *syllogism*, were defined by Aristotle (384–322 B.C.), a Greek philosopher. This form of reasoning makes use of (1) a statement of a general law (called a *major premise*), (2) a statement assigning a particular zone of interest to the general law (called a *minor premise*), and (3) a statement of *conclusion* which applies the general law to the specific zone of interest.

Illustration 11–1. The ability to make sound decisions at the right time is a distinguishing mark of the engineer. His knowledge and his ability to apply problem solving techniques aid him in the decision making process. (Courtesy Alexander Hamilton Institute)

Example: Major Premise. The volume of all spheres can be determined by the relationship $V = \pi D^3/6$, where D is the diameter of the sphere.
Minor Premise. A ball is a sphere.
Conclusion. The volume of a ball can be found by applying the relationship $V = \pi D^3/6$, where D is the diameter of the ball.

An obvious limitation of this form of reasoning is that the statements of the *major* and *minor premises* may not always be free from error. If an untruth is assumed as a *major* or *minor premise,* for example, the *conclusion* will most likely also be in error. Only by chance could the *conclusion* be a true statement. Thus this form of reasoning is most useful when the *major* and *minor premises* have been proved by experimentation for all possible situations. It also follows that deductive reasoning generally is not useful for the discovering of basic laws, but it may be useful in finding new applications of proven laws.

Undoubtedly complete adherence to the doctrine of deductive reasoning during the Middle Ages was a primary reason for the barrenness of achievement in physical sciences and engineering during this particular period of history. However, mathematics was not so limited because of its basic nature. Mathematics is a process of reasoning based upon fundamental concepts or premises, the parts of which are connected by the process of syllogism, or deductive reasoning.

In using deductive reasoning one must be very careful that the major premise identified is in fact true without exception. The person who accepts someone else's general statement that "there are no poisonous snakes in Henderson County" as being literally true, and then is bitten by one of the few rattlesnakes remaining, is a victim of a faulty premise. A second pitfall concerns the identification of a minor premise that in actuality is not correctly included within the major premise. For example, all $20 Federal Reserve notes are legal tender in the United States. However, a particular $20 note may be refused because it is a counterfeit bill and therefore not covered by the major premise. Although completely honest in his intent, one could violate the law by using the counterfeit money.

Inductive Reasoning

Methods of inductive reasoning, or *truth by experiment,* have been practiced to some degree since the beginning of man. However, Aristotelian logic was long the accepted authority, and it was not until the thirteenth century that a revolt against deductive logic was successfully launched. Processes of inductive reasoning were first set forth by Roger Bacon (1214–1294) and later amplified by Francis Bacon (1561–1626). This form of reasoning is based upon the premise that if two or more things agree with one another in one or more respects, they will likely agree in still other respects; that things which are true of certain individual items within a class will be true of the entire class; and phenomena which are true at certain times will be true in similar environments at all other times. This is reasoning from a part to a whole, from the particular to the general, and from the individual to the universal.

The aim of inductive reasoning is to arrive at general conclusions sufficiently invariant to be used as major premises in processes of deductive reasoning. Verification and identification of the behavior pattern is achieved by experiment. In many instances too few experiments are performed to give absolute assurance of the truth, and a confidence level of less than 100 per cent is the result. This brings about the use of statistics and probability to determine the most likely performance that can be expected in a particular situation. As with deductive reasoning, there are two pitfalls in using inductive reasoning. First, in an experiment, *"Have the observations been made under true environmental conditions?,"* and second, *"Have enough observations been made to establish the degree of probability that the circumstances require?"*[1]

It is only by the processes of inductive reasoning that general laws and new scientific truths can be discovered. Consequently it is only in this way that the major premises necessary for deduction can be found.

REASONING AND PROBLEM SOLVING

Engineers and scientists must master both the inductive or experimental method and the deductive method of logic, since the two processes of reasoning are complementary. Ordinarily a person does not by choice think only by deduction or induction. Rather, he will alternate from one form of logic to the other as he moves through an analysis. It is of considerable value, however, to know which type of reasoning to use in a given situation. Perhaps of even more value is the ability to recognize false premises or improper experimental methods that may have been employed in the processes of analysis.

Order of Action in the Problem Solving Process

Engineers who have mastered the engineering method of problem solving are considerably more successful in their work than are people who have not been trained in this technique. In the past many engineering problems were of such routine nature that a resort to deductive reasoning would suffice, and premises of deduction could be taken from handbooks. However, many of the engineering problems of today cannot be solved by mere "handbook techniques." Experimentation, research, and development have indeed become significant activities in today's world.

Regardless of the complexity of a problem or the subject area within which the problem might arise, the *method* of solution used by the engineer will probably follow a general pattern similar to that represented by Figure 11–4. Each part of this "cyclic" process will be described in more detail, but first two general characteristics of the process should be recognized:

1. Although the process conventionally moves in a clockwise direction, Figure 11–4, there is continual "feedback" within the cycle.

2. The method of solution is a repetitious process that may be continuously refined through any desired number of cycles.

The concept of *feedback* is not new. For example, *feedback* is used by the human body to evaluate the result of actions that have been taken. The eye sees something bright that appears desirable and the brain sends a command to the hand and fingers to secure it. However, if the bright object is also hot, upon touching the nerves in the fingers "feed back" information to the brain with the message that

[1] Edward Hodnett, *The Art of Problem Solving,* Harper, New York, (1955), p. 137.

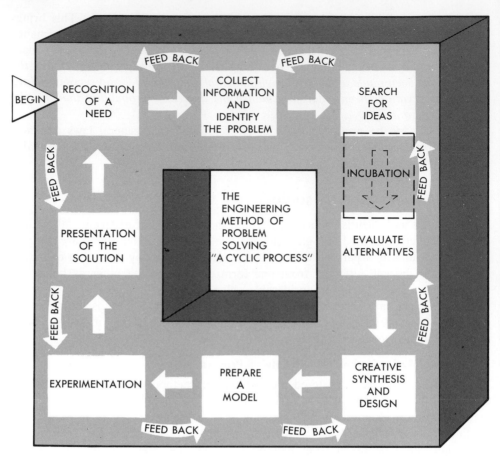

Figure 11—4.

"contact with this object will be injurious," and pain is registered to emphasize this fact. The brain reacts to this new information and sends another command to the fingers to release contact with the object. Upon completion of the feedback loop the fingers release the object.

As another example a thermostat, as part of a heating or cooling system, is a "feedback" device, since a changing temperature condition produces a response from the thermostat to tend to alter the change.

The speed of movement through the problem solving cycle is a function of many factors, and they change with each problem. Considerable time may be spent at any point within the cycle, and in other situations very little time may be consumed within steps. Thus, the problem solving process is a dynamic and constantly changing process that provides allowance for the individuality and capability of the user.

Recognition of a Need and Identification of the Problem

The first two steps in the problem solving process are the most important. First, the engineer must be sensitive to the changing condition of his environment, and he must be constantly aware that his immediate surrounding environment is but a small single point of experience which is located within the vast expanse of the universe. The engineer must be able to perceive that a *need* does in fact exist within his own environment. Only then is he ready to give consideration to identification and definition of the particular problem whose solution will satisfy the specific need that he has already recognized. Nothing is more frustrating than for him to solve a problem and then to find that the solution did not satisfy the need and that he had, in fact, been working on the wrong problem all of the time. Figure 11–5 is a diagrammatic representation of these relationships. It should be recognized that the engineer's design is but *one* possible solution to the identified problem. Many other satisfactory designs also probably exist.

The story is told of how a student in a physics class, whom we shall call Henry, was given the assignment of determining the height of his school building by using a small laboratory barometer. Much to the teacher's chagrin, Henry took the barometer, thought a moment, tied a long piece of string to it, and then lowered it to the ground from the roof of the building. He then quickly measured the length of the string and gave the teacher his answer. Unfortunately the teacher was not pleased with Henry's performance and asked him to obtain the solution by "the

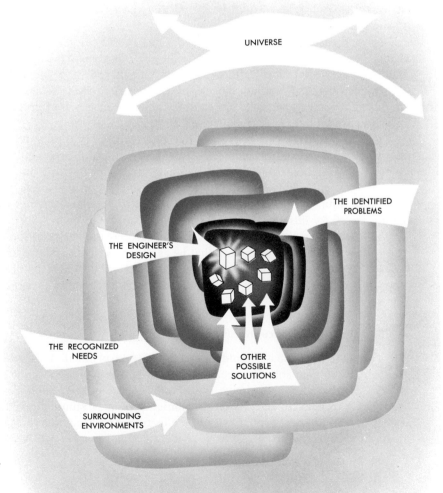

Figure 11–5.

obvious" method. Henry thought a few moments more and then took the barometer outside in the sunlight. By using a protractor and standing the barometer vertically and noting the length of its shadow and then comparing it with the length of the building shadow, he once again calculated the height of the building and verified his first solution. The teacher seemed even more irritated with Henry's efforts and tersely instructed him to use a "scientific" method to obtain the solution and "do it quickly." Henry thought and thought. Finally, he asked for a stopwatch and once again he climbed to the roof. He dropped the barometer from the roof into the fountain on the ground below. By carefully timing the free-fall of the instrument and substituting into the equation, $S = V_1 t + \frac{at^2}{2}$, he obtained an answer that verified the other two solutions. This time the teacher was very angry with Henry and told him that unless he got the *precise* answer by *the* "correct" method that he would fail the laboratory work. By this time Henry was completely confused and frustrated, and not knowing what the teacher wanted, he decided that he needed some "outside" help. Thereupon he took the barometer to the basement, traded it to the building superintendent for a set of architectural and engineering drawings of the building and within a few minutes he gave the teacher the *precise* answer that he had requested. It is said that the teacher collapsed of apoplexy at this point.

In each case the young student had "determined the height of the building by using the small laboratory barometer." In each instance he had obtained a seemingly acceptable solution—although none of them had been found by *the method* that the teacher had in mind. Too many people react as the teacher did and refuse to recognize or use perfectly acceptable designs because they were not the types of solutions that had been preconceived in their minds.

It is also much easier for one to recognize that "he has a problem" than to identify "just what the problem is." The most successful problem solvers are able to see their situation from different vantage points and to bring into focus a definition of "the real problem"—the problem whose solution will bring about the most satisfying result to the identified need. *Successful problem solving does not begin with a search for answers; it begins with the flexibility of your perception, with your ability to ask the right questions.*[2] By asking certain strategic questions, the engineer can collect additional information that he can then evaluate and use in the identification of the problem. In large measure the person who is able to discern the most appropriate questions to ask is the person who will be most successful as a problem solver.

Search for Ideas, Incubation, and Evaluation of Alternatives

The search for ideas should be deliberate and planned. It is a very important part of the problem solving process. If such a search is not consciously carried out, many desirable and imaginative ideas will be overlooked. Such a search should not be left to chance, since several techniques of idea stimulation are easy to use (see Chapter 12) and are known to be effective. The accumulation of ideas should begin as soon as the problem has been identified *but not before*. All too frequently,

[2] *Problem Solving,* Arthur D. Little, Inc., Cambridge, Mass., p. 1.

when confronted with a difficulty, many people will hurriedly grasp for ideas without first having recognized the need or identified the problem. *Such a tendency must be resisted.*

It is also of utmost importance that the search for ideas be a search without evaluation of the worth of the individual ideas. Evaluation is certainly needed later, but such judgment should be brought into play after the passage of a period of time. During this lapse, which has been called the "period of incubation," the subconscious is allowed freedom to wander. The use of the subconscious is also called intuition. Many testify to the fact that after such a period of freedom, insight and inspiration are more likely to emerge. The imagination seems to work best when the mind is unwearied and unrestrained. Of course, insight may occur at any time, and it does not necessarily always follow a period of incubation. However, it is known that insight and illumination do occur most often when one has immersed himself in a problem to the extent that he has become fatigued (and in some cases frustrated) and then has laid the problem to one side for a time.

It is difficult to search for ideas and consciously to defer judgment of those ideas until a later time. However, the value of the "deferment of judgment" principle has been proven many times. By deferring judgment a greater number of imaginative ideas can be collected, and the probability of obtaining an idea of great value is increased.

The practicability and theoretical soundness of each idea generated must now be determined. Previous to this point in the problem solving process the engineer was only concerned with the "quantity and originality" of ideas, but now he must be primarily concerned with the "quality or feasibility" of the ideas. Judgment of their worth will not depend upon the immediate usefulness of the ideas but rather upon where the ideas may lead. Few ideas are practical within themselves. However, a single idea may form the nucleus of a new process or design that the engineer can bring into being by expansion, minification, extension, modification, combination, or by otherwise altering in some way the original thought. Because of the nature of the educational process that engineering students experience, they become considerably more skilled in the evaluation of ideas and alternatives than they do in the birth of creative ideas. Although both abilities are very important to the engineer, neither should obscure the other.

Creative Synthesis and Design

The heart of the engineering method of problem solving lies in the creative synthesis of ideas and alternatives into an effective design. During this phase of the process the ideas and alternatives that have seemed most profitable to investigate are merged to form a useful solution to the identified problem. The data collected earlier can now be used in this design phase to bring about a specific solution for the specific purpose that has been set forth.

Although novel ideas frequently make their appearance when the conscious mind is not actively seeking them, we should recognize that most of the engineer's inspirational ideas are the result of new combinations and rearrangements of old thoughts which have already been stored within the subconscious. If this were not so, poems in Chinese might be written spontaneously by poets who are unfamiliar with the Chinese language; new mathematical theorems might be revealed in the dreams of Mexican bullfighters; and tomorrow's Chicago newspaper headlines might appear as visions today in the minds of uneducated fishermen in Greece. We recognize that none of these events are likely to happen. Neither is the engineer, regardless of how creative he may be, likely to produce new and useful ideas that lie beyond the realm of his experience. This fact does not, of course, rule out the use of inductive and deductive reasoning by the engineer in extending and applying his knowledge to new situations.

Understanding is necessary for design. It is said that "A man has a certain degree of understanding of an automobile when he can drive one, a higher degree of understanding when he can repair one, and a still higher degree of understanding when he can design one."[3]

The engineer must be skilled in deliberately and creatively refining, combining, and synthesizing his ideas into useful designs. In large measure his success will be proportional to his understanding of man and nature and his skill in obtaining a final design that is both simple and functional.

SIMPLIFYING ASSUMPTIONS AND PREPARATION OF A MODEL

Generally the engineer will not attempt to find the *perfect* solution to an identified problem, since finding the *perfect* solution would in most instances involve the expenditure of an inordinate sum of money over an extended period of time. Engineering is a profession that deals in realism. As such, it gives recognition to the value of time, money, materials, and human effort. Therefore, the engineer will strive to provide his employer or client with the best possible solution to a given problem within the capability and resources that are available. Some problems might have a great number of solutions. However, the engineer cannot spend several years in investigating, for example, the types of materials and loading conditions for a highway bridge . . . . not to speak of the unlimited number of variations that would exist if a number of sites were considered. Therefore, the engineer will accept certain simplifying assumptions or approximations that limit the scope of the design.

Unlike some other professionals, such as doctors or lawyers, the engineer does not usually work directly with the problem that he has identified. Instead, he will construct an *idealized model* of the real situation, and then he will work with this model to achieve what he believes to be an acceptable solution. Finally he will experiment with his model and test its effectiveness in satisfying the need that he originally found to be present. The *idealized model* is nothing more than an image of the real situation as visualized by the engineer. It is not reality. It may take on the form of a sketch, chart, geometrical diagram, mathematical equation, computer program, scale model, simulation device, or some other type of representation that may be substituted for the real situation for purposes of predicting behavior and simplifying the analysis.

The use of models to represent circumstances and to predict future behavior is

---

[3] Marshall Walker, *The Nature of Scientific Thought*, Prentice-Hall, Englewood Cliffs, N.J., (1963), p. 1.

not an unusual procedure in other walks of life. For example, each year thousands of school boys who engage in sports study diagrams that are composed of circles, squares, triangles, curved and straight lines, and other similar symbols. These diagrams represent to them actions which are anticipated in some future football or basketball game. Such geometrical models are limited because they are two-dimensional and they do not allow for strengths, weaknesses, and imaginative decisions of the individual athletes. However, their use has been proved to be quite valuable in simulating the outcome of small time-segments of the game and in predicting the eventual outcome of the contest. Other types of models such as the tackling dummy, the blocking sled, the automatic pitcher, and the punching bag have also proved their usefulness in training athletes to cope with circumstances that have been predicted to occur in future athletic events.

An *idealized model* may emphasize the whole of a system and minimize its component parts, or it may be designed to represent only some particular part of the system and ignore the remainder. In selecting an *idealized model* the engineer must recognize that he is merely simplifying or limiting the complexity of the problem in order that he can apply known laws of science in his analysis. *In actuality, the idealization chosen may deviate considerably from the true condition.* Consequently the engineer's solution for the model may or may not be an acceptable solution to the real problem. The engineer must therefore view his answers with respect to the assumptions he made initially in preparing his *idealized model.* If the assumptions were in error, or if their importance was underestimated, then the engineer's analysis will probably not approximate or predict true conditions very closely. Thus, the usefulness of the model to predict future actions must be verified by the engineer. This verification is accomplished by experimentation and testing of the model. Refinement of the model and verification by experimentation are continued until an acceptable representation of the real phenomena is obtained. The design of the model must be the product of creative action by the engineer, but the determination of the behavior or performance of the model will follow a pattern of deductive analysis. In given situations some types of models are more useful to the engineer than other types. A discussion of some of the general types of models that engineers use is given below.

TYPES OF IDEALIZED MODELS

The Mathematical Model

A mathematical model can be established for a given situation if the problem has been previously described in words or by use of sketches or diagrams. Mathematics is a means of communication that originated as an abstraction from empirical experience concerning the physical world. Originally the mathematical symbols and operations that were used were concerned with visible objects and processes in nature. Later it was found that the same symbols and operations could also be used in combination to represent hypothetical situations not necessarily descriptive of any physical object. In this way the behavior and characteristics of complex phenomena could be studied.

As an example, Sir Isaac Newton (1642–1727) expressed several basic laws that he believed to govern the motion of particles. His second law was stated as follows:

> *When an external unbalanced force acts on a particle of mass, the motion of the particle will be changed. The particle will be accelerated. Its rate of change in motion will be in the direction of the unbalanced force and will be proportional to it.*

This statement would be very cumbersome and even difficult to use in the printed form shown above. However, if mathematical symbols are used to represent some of the parts of the hypothesis, it becomes much easier to work with.

Stated mathematically: (for motion in one direction)
$$\frac{F_1}{a_1} = \frac{F_2}{a_2} = \frac{F_3}{a_3} = \frac{F_n}{a_n} = \text{a constant}$$

Where: F_1, F_2, F_3, etc., are the external unbalanced forces acting on a particle, and a_1, a_2, a_3, etc., are the consequential accelerations of the particle.

The relationship is most commonly expressed as $F = Ma$, where M represents the invariant quantity, *mass*.

Another example can be taken from electrical engineering. There is a well known relation of electrical quantities in a circuit which says that *the ratio of the voltage difference across a conductor to the current passing through it is a constant.* This may be expressed as:

$$\frac{\text{Voltage}}{\text{Current}} = \text{a constant called } \textit{resistance}$$

or

$$\frac{V}{I} = R, \text{ and } V = IR$$

A mathematical model is the most generally applicable and most powerful form of model that the engineer can use. It is also the easiest to understand and manipulate once it has been written.

The Diagram

A favorite type of model that is used by the engineer is the *diagram*. Typical forms of diagrams are the *block diagram,* the *energy diagram,* the *electrical diagram,* and the *free body diagram.* Some attention should be given to each of these forms.

The *block diagram,* Figure 11–4, is a generalized approach at examining the whole problem and identifying its main components. Such a diagram is particularly useful in indicating the relationships and interdependencies of component parts of the problem. This type of diagram is particularly useful in the early stages of design work and where representation by a mathematical model would be very difficult to accomplish, Illustration 11–2 is an example of a block diagram in which electrical subassemblies are drawn as blocks, and the connecting lines between blocks indicate the flow of information in the whole assembly. This type of presentation is widely used to lay out large or complicated systems—particularly those involving servo-electrical and mechanical devices. No attempt is made on the drawing to detail the inner circuits of any of the subassemblies pictured. This does not, however, provide a substitute for a mathematical model.

The *energy diagram* is particularly useful in the study of thermodynamic systems involving mass and energy flow. Before drawing such a diagram the engineer should set forth simplifying assumptions and selection of boundaries and operating conditions. This type of diagram is a modification of the block diagram. Some examples of the use of an *energy diagram* are given in Figures 11–6 and 11–7.

Example: A quantity of high-temperature steam flows into a turbine at high pressure, expands in the turbine while doing work on the turbine rotor, and then is exhausted at low pressure. Draw an *energy diagram* of this situation. The results may be as shown in Figure 11–6.

Example: Draw an *energy diagram* showing how nuclear power can be used to operate a submarine. The results may be as shown in Figure 11–7.

The *electrical diagram* is a specialized type of model used in the analysis of electrical problems. This form of *idealized model* represents the existence of particular electrical circuits by utilizing conventional symbols for brevity. These diagrams may be of the most elementary type, or they may be highly complicated and require many hours of engineering time in preparation. In any case, however, they are representations or models in symbolic language of an electrical assembly.

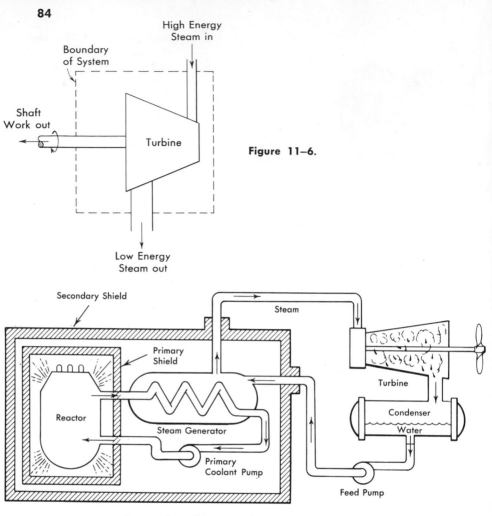

High Energy
Steam in

Boundary
of System

Shaft
Work out

Turbine

Figure 11–6.

Low Energy
Steam out

Secondary Shield

Steam

Primary
Shield

Turbine

Reactor

Condenser
Water

Steam Generator

Primary
Coolant Pump

Feed Pump

Courtesy: General Dynamics, Electric Boat Division

Figure 11–7. Diagrammatic sketch showing how nuclear power can be used to operate a submarine. (Courtesy General Dynamics, Electric Boat Division.)

Figure 11–8 shows an electrical diagram of a photoelectric tube that is arranged to operate a relay. Notice that the diagram details only the essential parts in order to provide for electrical continuity and thus is an idealization that has been selected for purposes of simplification.

The *free-body diagram* is a diagrammatical representation of a physical system which has been removed from all other surrounding bodies or systems for purposes of examination. It may be drawn to represent a complex system or any smaller part of it. This form of *idealized model* is most useful in showing the effect of forces that act upon a system.

The boundaries of a *free-body diagram,* real or imaginary, should be drawn such that they enclose the system under study. All force actions external to the boundaries that act on the "free-body" should be represented by force vectors on the diagram. Force actions internal to the boundaries should be ignored, since the system is usually analyzed as a whole. Extraneous detail of the complex environment

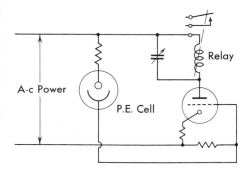

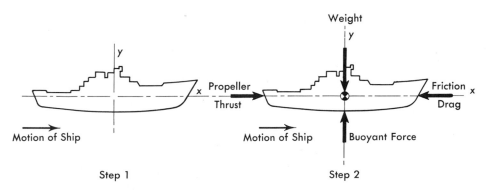

Figure 11–8. A simple photoelectric tube relay circuit.

Figure 11–9. Step 1. Draw the boundaries of the system. Step 2. Show on the same figure external forces which are acting on the boundaries.

should not appear on the *free-body diagram*. Rather, the diagram should include only the detail that is significant to the problem.

Of course a *free-body diagram* is merely an idealized model of the real situation, and it is imaginary in every sense. Such an idealized condition does not exist in nature, but it is assumed to so exist for purposes of the analysis. The usefulness of the diagram depends upon how well it represents the real situation. The following example problems are typical of some problem types that the student may encounter in the solving of engineering problems.

Example: Draw a free-body diagram of a ship which is moving forward in the water.

SOLUTION: It is not necessary that the free-body diagram be drawn to exact scale, since the shape of the *idealized model* is only an imaginary concept. Proceed in two steps as shown in Figure 11–9.

EXPLANATION: In the most general sense, the external forces acting on the *idealized model* are four in number: a forward thrust, which acts at the ship's propeller; a friction drag, which acts in such manner as to retard motion; a buoyant force, which keeps the ship afloat; and the ship's weight, which in simplification may be considered to be acting through the center of gravity of the ship.

NOTE: The symbol ☻ is used to denote the location of the center of gravity of an *idealized model*. Also notice that a coordinate system, as applied to the free-body diagram, is very useful for purposes of orientation. The diagram shown would be an analysis of the relationships between the weight and buoyant force and between the thrust and drag. However, it would not, for example, be useful for determining the loads on the ship's engine mounts. Another model (free body diagram) would now be required.

Example: Draw a free-body diagram of a four-wheel drive automobile being driven up an incline, as shown in Figure 11–10.

EXPLANATION: Always show the system under consideration in its true and realistic position in space. For example, it would have been awkward to have shown the automobile as being on a horizontal surface, since it is in actuality moving up an incline.

GENERAL SUGGESTIONS FOR DRAWING FREE-BODY DIAGRAMS

To aid the student in learning to draw free-body diagrams, the following suggestions are given:

1. Free Bodies. Be certain that the body is *free* of all surrounding objects. Draw the body so it is *free*. Do not show a supporting surface, but rather show only the force vector which replaces that surface. Do not rotate the body from its original position, but rather rotate the axes if necessary. Show all forces and label them. Show all needed dimensions and angles.

2. Force Components. Forces are often best shown in their component forms. When replacing a force by its components, select the most convenient directions for the components. Never show both a force and its components by solid-line vectors; use broken-line vectors for one or the other since the force *and* its components do not occur simultaneously.

3. Weight Vectors. Show the weight vector as a vertical line with its tail or point at the center of gravity, and place it so that it interferes least with the remainder of the drawing. It should always be drawn vertically.

4. Refer to the Free-Body Diagram. Each step of the solution should have a clear cross reference to the free body to which it pertains.

5. Direction of Vectors. The free-body diagram should represent the facts as nearly as possible. If a pull on the free body occurs, place the tail of the vector at the actual point of application and let the point of the vector be in the true direction of the pull. Likewise, if a push occurs on the free body, the vector should show the true direction, and the point of the arrow should be placed at the point of application. Force vectors on free-body diagrams are not usually drawn to scale but may be drawn proportionate to their respective magnitudes.

6. Free-Body Diagram of Whole Structure. This should habitually be the first free-body examined in the solution of any problem. Many problems cannot be solved without this first consideration. After the free-body of the whole structure or com-

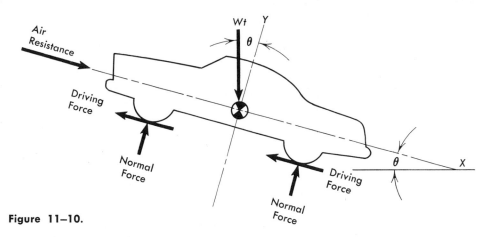

Figure 11–10.

plex has been considered, select such members or subassemblies for further free-body diagrams as may lead to a direct solution.

7. Two-Force Members. When a two-force member is in equilibrium, the forces are equal, opposite, and collinear. If the member is in compression, the vectors should point toward each other; if a member is in tension, they should point away from each other.

8. Three-Force Members. When a member is in equilibrium and has only three forces acting on it, the three forces are always concurrent, if they are not parallel. In analyzing a problem involving a three-force member, one should recall that any set of concurrent forces may be replaced by a resultant force. Hence, if a member in equilibrium has forces acting at three points, it is a three-force member, regardless of the fact that the force applied at one or more points may be replaced by two or more components.

9. Concurrent Force System. For a concurrent force system the size, shape, and dimensions of the body are neglected, and the body is considered to be a particle.

Example: Draw a free body of point A, as shown in Figure 11–11.

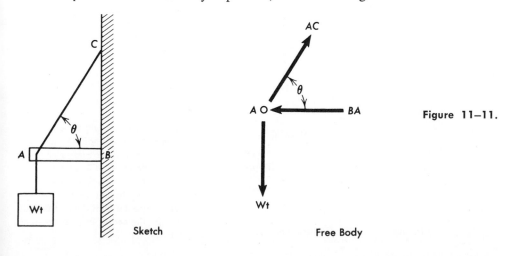

Figure 11–11.

Sketch

Free Body

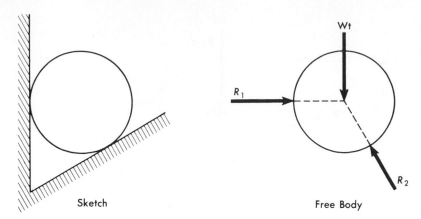

Sketch   Free Body

Figure 11–12.

Situation	Free-Body	Explanation

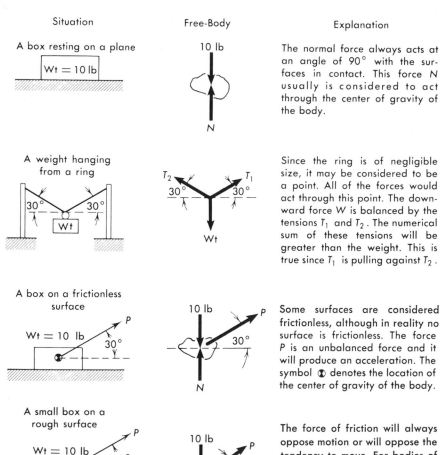

A box resting on a plane — 10 lb / N — The normal force always acts at an angle of 90° with the surfaces in contact. This force N usually is considered to act through the center of gravity of the body.

A weight hanging from a ring — T_2, T_1, 30°, 30°, Wt — Since the ring is of negligible size, it may be considered to be a point. All of the forces would act through this point. The downward force W is balanced by the tensions T_1 and T_2. The numerical sum of these tensions will be greater than the weight. This is true since T_1 is pulling against T_2.

A box on a frictionless surface — 10 lb, P, 30°, N — Some surfaces are considered frictionless, although in reality no surface is frictionless. The force P is an unbalanced force and it will produce an acceleration. The symbol ⊕ denotes the location of the center of gravity of the body.

A small box on a rough surface — 10 lb, P, 30°, F, N — The force of friction will always oppose motion or will oppose the tendency to move. For bodies of small size, the *moment effect*[4] of the friction force may be disregarded and the friction and normal forces may be considered to act through the center of gravity of the body.

Figure 11–13.

[4] See page 109 for an explanation of moments.

10. Pin Joints.   A free-body diagram of the pin itself should be drawn when it lends to simplicity of the solution. Pin connections usually may be considered to be frictionless.

11. Reaction between Surfaces.   Some problems involve *smooth surfaces* (an imaginary concept) that are considered to offer no frictional resistance to motion. For bodies in equilibrium at rest, this concept is both a useful and practical approximation. Pins and the members they join are in contact on a surface, and the reaction between the surfaces is perpendicular to the common tangent plane at the point of contact. Thus, if a cylinder rests on a plane, the reaction at the point of contact will pass through the center of the cylinder, as shown in Figure 11–12.

Additional examples are given in Figures 11–13 and 11–14 to illustrate situations that the engineer may encounter, together with the resulting free-body diagrams which may be drawn as models to represent the situations.

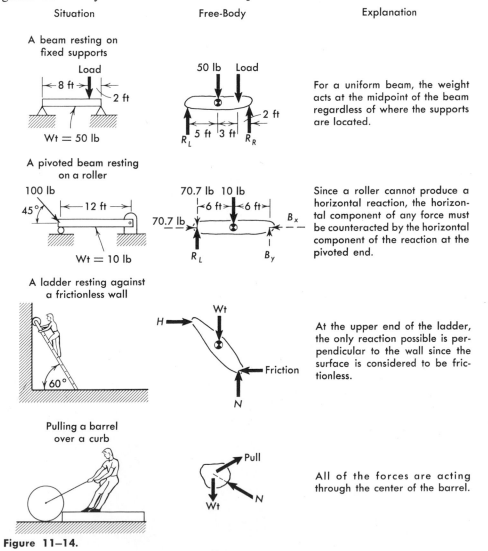

Figure 11–14.

The Scale Model

Scale models are used in various problem solving situations, and they are particularly useful where the system under consideration is very large and complex or very small and difficult to observe. They are also used by the engineer in many instances where a mathematical model is either impossible or impractical.

A *scale model* is an idealized replica, usually three-dimensional, of the system, subsystem, or component being studied. The idealization may be constructed to any desired scale and the final *scale model* may be larger in size, the same size, or much smaller in size than the actual design.

Such projects as dam or reservoir construction, highway and freeway interchange design, factory layout, and aerodynamic investigations are particularly adaptable to study by using this type of idealized model. In some cases the scale model is not instrumented, Illustration 11–3, but component parts of the model can be moved about to represent changing conditions within the system. Of considerably more usefulness, however, are those scale models which are instrumented and subjected to environmental and load conditions that closely resemble reality, Illustration 11–4. In such cases the models are tested and experimental data are recorded by the engineer. From an analysis of these data, predictions of the behavior of the real system can be made.

Illustration 11–3. Exact scale models are valuable aids to the engineer in acquainting others with design and operating procedures such as this model of an ammonia-nitrogen plant located in Taiwan. (Courtesy Allied Chemical Corporation.)

Illustration 11–4. Pictured above is a spacecraft which is located in a 30-foot diameter space simulation chamber to permit engineers to investigate problems of actual temperature and vacuum conditions which will be encountered in space. The model spacecraft is altered after each actual space mission to represent more closely the behavior of the vehicle in space. (Courtesy McDonnell Aircraft Corporation.)

Illustration 11–5. Centrifuge used to simulate space conditions for training astronauts. (Courtesy Timken Roller Bearing Company.)

By using a scale model the final design can be checked for accuracy prior to actual construction of the design. Although scale models often cost many thousands of dollars, they are of relatively minor expense, considering the total cost of a particular project. Also, a scale model frequently may be constructed and tested in a fraction of the time necessary to build the original system.

The Simulation Model

A *simulation model* may be used to represent the behavior of environmental conditions, Illustration 11–5. When experimentation is performed on a *scale model,* it is referred to as *simulation.* Such experimentation makes it possible for the engineer to evaluate alternatives and to make adjustments in his design with minimum expense, loss of time, and danger to life. The use of *simulation* devices, as much as any other single factor, is credited with minimizing the fatality rate in the "Manned Space Program," presently being conducted by the United States.

Computer simulation has also become very important to the engineer. Analog computers are used in those cases where electrical impulses can be made to behave in a manner analogous to that of the real object or process being simulated. Digital computers are used where the design or process can be broken down into a multitude of small limited-choice decisions. In addition to obtaining a realistic appraisal of the actual design performance, the computer can simulate years of real time in a very few hours because of the exceptionally fast speed with which a digital computer can accomplish a given calculation. Simulation of the passage of time by any other means is very difficult for the engineer to achieve.

Illustration 11–6. Experimentation and verification of the performance of idealized models are important factors to the engineer. Here an engineer is working with a simulation model of the human body which he is using to verify automotive design calculations that he has made. (Courtesy Chrysler Corporation.)

EXPERIMENTATION, VERIFICATION, AND PRESENTATION OF THE SOLUTION

Much engineering work is concerned with experimentation for the purpose of verifying design calculations. As suggested above a majority of such testing involves a determination of the degree of success or failure of an idealized model to achieve desired standards. Frequently feed-back of the test results will cause the engineer to re-examine his model and to make alterations or adjustments in its design. By repeating this process over and over, an idealized model which closely approximates the real-life situation can be found, Illustration 11–6.

Since the real-life situation cannot be known in advance in many instances, the engineer's model serves also to predict the future. For example, since man had never before experienced the effects of space travel, the engineer could only anticipate such consequences by experimentation involving various types of models that he designed for this purpose. The success of man's first flight into space and his safe return is a tribute to the engineer's abilities in designing and testing models and in simulating man's reactions within a foreign environment.

It has been said that "the proof of the pudding is in the eating." Certainly this is good advice for the engineer to follow. No idealized model or design, regardless of its sophistication or simplicity, is of value to the engineer unless it serves as a satisfactory answer to the need that was recognized originally. This is the final goal of the engineering method of problem solving, and this step serves to complete the cyclic problem solving process.

Problems

11–1. Draw a free-body diagram of the container for radioactive materials as shown in Illustration 11–7.

11–2. Draw a free-body diagram of the ballistic missile as shown in Illustration 11–8, p. 95.

11–3. Draw a free-body diagram of point Q as shown in Figure 11–15.

11–4. Draw a free-body diagram of the sphere shown in Figure 11–16.

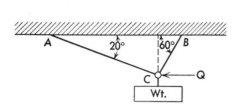

Figure 11–15.

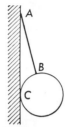

Figure 11–16.

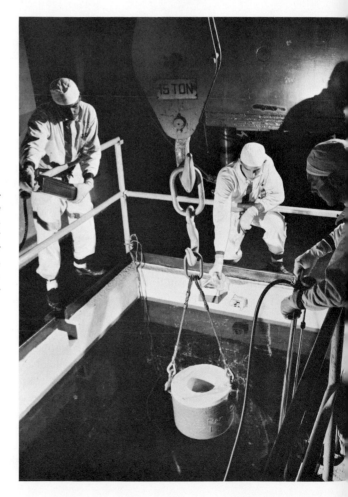

Illustration 11–7. Since radioactive materials must be handled with extreme care, the lowering of a container of radioactive products must be monitored continuously, using precision instruments. (Courtesy Westinghouse Electric Corporation)

11–5. Draw a free-body diagram of the sphere shown in Figure 11–17.

11–6. Draw a free-body diagram of the sphere shown in Figure 11–18.

11–7. Draw a free-body diagram of the sphere shown in Figure 11–19.

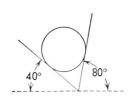

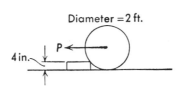

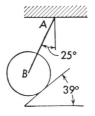

Figure 11–17.   **Figure 11–18.**   **Figure 11–19.**

11–8. Draw the free-body diagram of the horizontal beam shown in Figure 11–20.

11–9. Draw a free-body diagram of the horizontal bar shown in Figure 11–21.

11–10. Draw a thermodynamic system of an ordinary gas-fired hot water heater.

11–11. A water heater operates under steady-flow conditions such that a quantity

Illustration 11–8. Test stands for launching rockets and missiles are complex structures which have been designed so that all parts of the missile will be accessible for instrumentation checks prior to launching. (Reprinted from *Missiles and Rockets,* American Aviation Publications, Inc.)

Problems (continued)

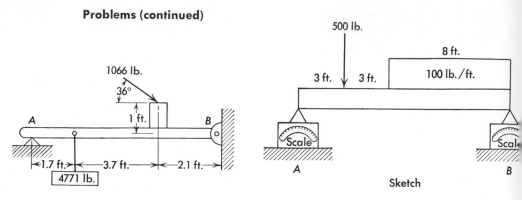

Figure 11–20.   Figure 11–21.

of entering low-temperature water is mixed with steam. The mixing takes place inside the heater and leaves the exit as one fluid. Draw a thermo-dynamic system to represent this process.

11–12. Draw a thermodynamic system of a vapor-compression refrigeration cycle.

11–13. A water heater operates under steady flow such that low-temperature water enters the heater, extracts heat from steam while inside the heater, and leaves the heater at an elevated temperature. The water and steam do not come in direct contact with each other. Draw a thermodynamic system to represent this process.

11–14. Draw an electrical circuit diagram containing two single-pole double-throw switches in such manner that a single light bulb may be turned on or off at either switch location.

11–15. Arrange three single-pole single-throw switches in an electrical circuit containing three light bulbs in such manner that one switch will turn on one of the bulbs, another switch will turn on two of the bulbs, and the third switch will turn on all three bulbs.

11–16. Show a thermodynamic system representing a simple refrigeration cycle.

11–17. A white oak beam is 18 ft long and 8 in. by 10 in. in cross section. What is its weight?

11–18. What will be the diameter of a tank 22.5 ft high that holds 1620 ft³ of water?

11–19. A cylindrical tank is 20.6 ft in diameter, 8 ft high, and contains 15,300 gal of water. What weight of water is contained in the tank?

11–20. A cylindrical tank is 20.8 ft in diameter, 8 ft high, and is made of steel 3/16 in. thick. What is the area of the side and bottom of the tank? What is the weight of the tank?

11–21. A storage vat is 100 yd long, 12 ft deep, and its width is 10 ft at the bottom and 15 ft at the top (trapezoidal cross section). The ends of the vat are vertical. Oil flows into the vat at a rate of 500 gpm. Find the time in hours that is required to fill the vat to a depth of 10 ft.

11–22. How many gallons of water will be contained in a horizontal pipe 10 in. in diameter and 15 ft long, if the water is 6 in. deep in the pipe?

11–23. Find the cost of 23 pieces of 2-in. by 10-in. yellow pine boards 12 ft long at $100 per 1000 fbm.

11–24. A white pine board is 14 ft long and 2 in. by 8 in. in cross section. How much will the board weigh? At $120 per 1000 fbm, what is its value?

11–25. A cast iron cone used in a machine shop is 10 in. in diameter at the bottom and 34 in. high. What is the weight of the cone?

11–26. How many cubic yards of soil will it take to fill a lot 63 ft wide by 100 ft deep if it is to be raised 3 ft in the rear end and gradually sloped to the front where it is to be 1½ ft deep?

11–27. A sphere whose radius is 1.42 in. is cut out of a solid cylinder 8.8 in. high and 7.8 in. in diameter. Find the volume cut away, in cubic inches. If the ball is steel, what does it weigh?

11–28. A container is 12 in. high, 10 in. in diameter at the top, and 6 in. in diameter at the bottom. What is the volume of this container in cubic inches? What is the weight of mercury that would fill this container?

11–29. A canal on level land is 19 mi long, 22 ft deep, and has a trapezoidal cross section. The distance across the canal at the top is 36 ft and across the bottom is 15 ft. Find: (a) the number of cubic yards of dirt that were removed to complete the canal; (b) the time in hours required to pump the canal full of water if the pump discharges 600 gpm and gates at either end are closed.

11–30. A cylindrical tank 7.50 ft in diameter and 15.9 ft long is lying with its axis horizontal. Compute the weight of kerosene when it is one-third full.

11–31. A container that is in the form of a right rectangular pyramid has the following dimensions: base 26 in. by 39 in., height 16 ft. This container has one-half of its volume filled with ice water. Neglect the weight of the container. Find the weight of the contents.

11–32. A hemispherical container 3 ft in diameter has half of its volume filled with lubricating oil. Neglecting the weight of the container, how much would the contents weigh if enough kerosene were added to fill the container to the brim?

11–33. Find the area in acres of a tract of land in the shape of a right triangle, one angle being 55°30′, and the shortest side being 1755 ft long. What length of fence will be needed to enclose the tract?

11–34. Points *A* and *B* are located on opposite corners of a building and are located so that they can be seen from point *C*. The distance *CA* is 256 ft and *CB* is 312 ft. The angle between lines *CA* and *CB* is 105°30′. How far apart are points *A* and *B*?

11–35. Find the area of a sheet of titanium 0.063 in. thick having dimensions as shown in Figure 11–22. What will be the approximate weight of the sheet of titanium?

11–36. A piece of sheet aluminum in the shape of a triangle has sides of 3.05 in. and 6.11 in., and the angle between these sides is 76°18′. (*a*) What are the other angles? (*b*) What is the area of the piece of metal?

11–37. In surveying, the determination of the distance *AB* is required. The given measurements are shown in Figure 11–23. What is the distance *AB*?

11–38. In a survey, an obstacle in the line *AB* is encountered. To determine the distance *AB,* the measurements shown in Figure 11–24 were made. What is the computed distance *AB*?

Problems (continued)

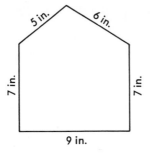

Figure 11–22.

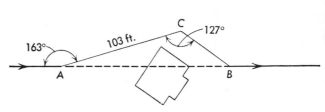

Figure 11–23.

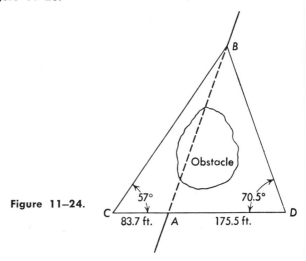

Figure 11–24.

11–39. Convert the following Fahrenheit temperatures to Celsius temperatures. (*a*) 68°, (*b*) 98.6°, (*c*) 156°, (*d*) 359°, (*e*) 711°, (*f*) 2880°, (*g*) 4.7 (10^4)°, (*h*) −5°, (*i*) −40°, (*j*) −255°.

11–40. Convert the following Celsius temperatures to Fahrenheit temperatures. (*a*) 20°, (*b*) 37°, (*c*) 155°, (*d*) 580°, (*e*) 8800°, (*f*) 1.22 (10^5)°, (*g*) −2°, (*h*) −40°, (*i*) −273°.

11–41. The temperature of liquid oxygen used as missile fuel is about −183°C. What is its temperature in degrees Fahrenheit?

11–42. The temperature of dry ice (solid carbon dioxide), used in shrinking metal parts to fit them together, is −78.5°C. What is the corresponding temperature in degrees Fahrenheit?

11–43. An air-storage tank used in windtunnel research has a volume of 138 ft³. How many cubic feet of air at atmospheric pressure will have to be pumped into it to raise the pressure to 185 psig?

11–44. A tight-fitting piston 3.77 in. in diameter in a closed cylinder compresses air from an initial pressure of 35 psig to 68 psig. If the final volume of the air is 14.58 in.³, what will be the distance the piston moves?

11–45. Natural gas in an underground pipe line 24 in. inside diameter is under a pressure of 375 psig. If this gas is allowed to expand to a pressure of 3.0 psig, what volume would the gas in a mile of high-pressure pipe occupy?

11–46. An open-end cylinder with the open end down is lowered into a lake. If the pressure due to water is 0.434 psi for each foot depth of water, how deep would the cylinder be lowered to reduce the volume of trapped air by one fifth its original volume?

11–47. The normal pressure of the atmosphere at sea level (14.7 psi) will support a column of mercury 29.92 in. high in a barometer. The atmospheric pressure changes approximately 0.1 in. of mercury for each 90 ft of elevation change at low elevations. What will be the approximate normal atmospheric pressure in psi at an elevation of 3050 ft above sea level?

11–48. An automobile tire is inflated to a pressure of 28 psig when the temperature is 51°F. After a period of driving, the temperature of the air in the tire has been raised to 125°F. What will be the gage pressure of the air?

11–49. Air that has been confined under a pressure of 5.0 psig in the cylinder of an air compressor is further compressed by a tight-fitting piston that decreases the volume from 0.89 ft³ to 0.27 ft³. At the same time the temperature of the air is raised from 43°F to 138°F. What will be the final gage pressure of the confined air?

11–50. A balloon used for meteorological research has a volume of 137 ft³. At the time it leaves the ground, the pressure of the gas inside the balloon is 3.0 ounces per in.² gage and the temperature is 88°F. It rises to a height where the temperature is −40°F and the pressure in the balloon is 6.88 psia. If the balloon expands freely, what will be the new volume?

11–51. A steel drum of oxygen shows a gage pressure of 2100 psig at a temperature of 95°F. What will be the gage pressure at a temperature of −12°F?

11–52. An open end cylinder 10 ft long is lowered into a tank of water with the open end down so that the lower end is at a depth of 9.65 ft. The temperature of the trapped air is 43°F. At what air temperature would the trapped air have expanded until it had displaced all the water which had risen inside the cylinder? The pressure due to water is 0.433 psi per ft of depth.

PROBLEMS IN STATIC MECHANICS

Mechanics is the physical science that describes and predicts the effects of forces acting on material bodies. The condition under study may be one of rest or one of motion. There are three specialized branches into which the general field of mechanics may be divided for more specific studies. These are:

1. Mechanics of rigid bodies
   a. Statics
   b. Dynamics
2. Mechanics of deformable bodies
3. Mechanics of fluids
   a. Compressible flow
   b. Incompressible flow

Our study here is concerned with an introduction to 1.*a.*, Static Mechanics, as a vehicle for the application of the engineering method of problem solution.

Fundamental Concepts and Definitions

Concepts used in our study of static mechanics are *force, space,* and *matter*. These concepts are basic and, as a frame of reference, should be accepted on the basis of our general experience. A *force* is the result of the interaction of two or more bodies and in our study here will be considered to be a localized vector quantity. A force may be evolved as the result of physical contact, or it may be developed at some distance—as is the case with magnetic and gravitational forces. *Space* is a region extending in all directions. It is associated with the location or position of a particle or of particles with respect to one another. *Matter* is a substance that occupies space.

A *particle* may be said to be a negligible amount of matter that occupies a single point in space. A *rigid* body is a body that is constructed entirely of particles that do not change their position in space with respect to each other. No real body is rigid. However, in many situations the deformation, or change in position of the particles, is very small and therefore would have a negligible effect upon the analysis. Such is the assumption in this chapter.

A *scalar* quantity is one that can be completely defined by giving its magnitude. Examples of scalar quantities are temperature, work, volume, time, speed, and energy. A *vector* quantity is one that must be described by direction, as well as magnitude, to define it completely. Vectors may be free in space, with no specific line of action, or localized to a unique point of application or fixed position in space. Examples of vector quantities are force, velocity, acceleration, displacement, and momentum. Scalars may be added, subtracted, etc., according to the ordinary laws of algebra. Vectors, on the other hand, must be handled according to principles of vector mathematics, which will be discussed later in this chapter. Force systems are said to be:

1. *Coplanar,* when all of the force vectors lie in the same plane (see Figure 11–25).

2. *Collinear,* when all forces act along the same line (see Figure 11–26).

3. *Concurrent,* when all the forces originate or intersect at a single point (see Figure 11–27).

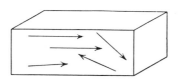

Coplanar Force System

Figure 11–25.

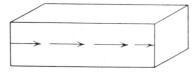

Collinear Force System

Figure 11–26.

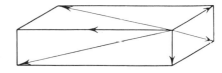

Concurrent Force System

Figure 11–27.

All force vectors should plainly show the sense or direction of force. This can best be done by the use of arrowheads on the point of the force. Space coordinate axes are frequently used to aid in positioning vector systems.

Example: A force of 150 lb$_f$ is pulling upward from a point at an angle of 30° with the horizontal (see Figure 11–28).

The length of the arrow in the above example was scaled (using an engineer's scale) to 1 in. equals 100 lb$_f$ and is 1½ in. long acting upward at an angle of 30° with the horizontal. In graphic work the arrow point should not extend completely to the end of the vector, since it is very easy to "overrun" the exact length of the measured line in the drawing of the arrowhead.

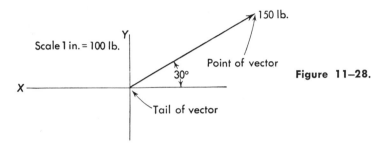

Figure 11–28.

In rigid-body mechanics the external effect of a force on a rigid body is independent of the point of application of the force along its line of action. Thus it would be considered immaterial whether a tractor pushed or pulled a box from a given position. The total effect on the box would be the same in either case. This is called the *Principle of Transmissibility* and will be used extensively in this chapter. This may be illustrated as shown in Figure 11–29.

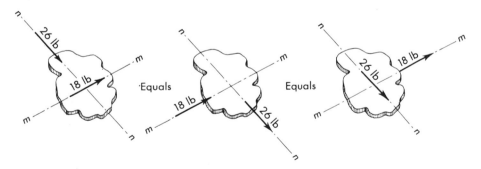

Figure 11–29.

Example: In each case the body is being acted upon by forces of 26 lb$_f$ and 18 lb$_f$. The total effect on the body is assumed to be the same for each example, since it is the line of action of a force which is significant, rather than its point of application.

Resolutions of Forces

In this initial study of static mechanics we shall deal mainly with concurrent, coplanar force systems. It is sometimes advantageous to combine two such forces into a single equivalent force, which we shall call a *resultant*. The original forces are called *components*.

Example: What single force R pulling at point O will have the same effect as components F_1 and F_2? (See Figure 11–30.)

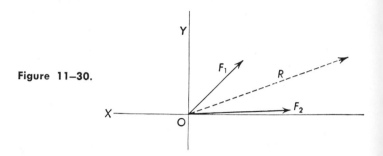

Figure 11–30.

There are several methods of combining these two components into a single resultant. Let us examine the *parallelogram method*, the *polygon of forces*, and the *rectangular component method*.

Parallelogram Method

1. Choose a suitable scale.
2. Lay out the two coplanar components to scale, pointing away from the point of intersection.
3. Using these two components as sides, construct a parallelogram.
4. Draw the diagonal through the point of intersection.
5. Measure the diagonal (which is the resultant of the two components) for magnitude (with engineer's scale) and direction (with protractor).

Example: Solve for the resultant of components F_1 and F_2 if they are separated by angle θ (see Figure 11–31).

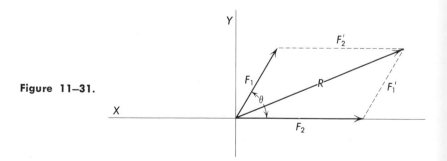

Figure 11–31.

Example: Two coplanar forces of 30 lb$_f$ and 40 lb$_f$, respectively, are at right angles to each other. Determine the magnitude of the resultant and the angle between the resultant and the 40-lb$_f$ force (see Figure 11–32). Lay out the two forces to scale as outlined above. The diagonal is measured to be 50 lb$_f$ and is located at an angle of 36.9° with the 40-lb$_f$ force.

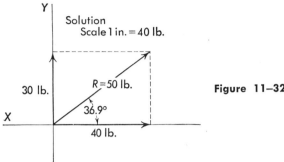

Figure 11–32.

Problems

Solve, using the parallelogram method.

11–53. Find the resultant of two concurrent forces of 1939 lb$_f$ and 1220 lb$_f$, respectively, if the angle between them is 20°; if the angle is 130°.

11–54. Find the resultant of two concurrent forces, one 320 lb$_f$ due east and the other 550 lb$_f$ S 30° E.

11–55. Force A is 450 lb$_f$. Force B is 325 lb$_f$ and acts at an angle of 54° with A. The forces are concurrent. What is the amount of the resultant and what angle does it make with force A?

11–56. Find the resultant of two concurrent components, one of 1225 lb$_f$ due west and the other of 1450 lb$_f$ S 30° E.

11–57. A heavy piece of machinery is being moved along a floor with two cables making an angle of 28° 30′ with each other. If the pulls are 45,000 and 25,000 lb$_f$, respectively, by what single force could they be replaced, and at what angle would the force act?

11–58. Find the resultant of a velocity of 150 mph due east and a velocity of 280 mph S 70° E. Use a scale of 1 in. equals 20 mph.

11–59. Three ropes are attached to a heavy body. If the first is pulled east by a force of 159 lb$_f$, the second by a force of 75 lb$_f$ 30° east of north, and the third north by a force of 108 lb$_f$, what is the resultant pull exerted on the body?

11–60. Three lines are connected to a missile. One line, having a tension of 1500 lb$_f$, runs due north; a second line, with a tension of 870 lb$_f$, runs S 75° W; a third line, with a tension of 1240 lb$_f$, runs N 58° E. Find the position and direction of a properly placed guy wire to brace the missile.

11–61. A man pulls straight ahead on a test sled with a force of 148 lb$_f$. If this man is replaced by two men, one pulling 36° to his left and the other pulling 20° to his right, what force must each of the new men exert if the sled is to move in the same direction?

Problems (continued)

11–62. A weight is held up by two cables that make angles of 50° and 25°, respectively, with the horizontal. Their resultant is vertical and equal to the weight which is 260 lb_f. Find the tension in each cable.

11–63. Two men are raising a 100 lb_f container from a reactor by means of two ropes. Find the force each man is exerting on his rope if one rope makes a 15° angle with the vertical and the other makes a 25° angle with the vertical.

Polygon of Forces

If two or more forces (or components) are concurrent and coplanar, their resultant can be determined by a faster and more convenient method known as the *polygon of forces*. In order to apply this method, proceed as follows:

1. Select a suitable scale.

2. Lay out one of the components with its correct magnitude and direction. At the tip of this component construct very lightly a small space coordinate system.

3. From the origin of this new space coordinate system lay out another component, placing the tail of the second component against the point of the first component.

4. Proceed in like manner until all components are used once (and only once).

5. Draw a vector from the original origin to the tip of the last component. This vector represents the *resultant* of the force system in both magnitude and direction.

Example: Solve for the resultant of the vector system shown in Figure 11–33.

Observe that R_1 is the resultant of the 116-lb_f component and the 368-lb_f component, R_2 is the resultant of R_1 and the 415-lb_f component, and R_3 is the resultant of R_2 and the 301-lb_f component. We see that R_3 (410-lb_f at $\theta = 28°$), then, is the resultant of all the components.

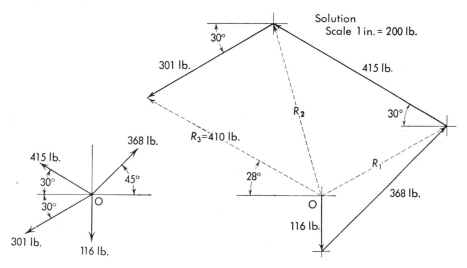

Figure 11–33.

It makes no difference in what sequence the components are placed in series. The resultant will be the same in magnitude and direction. In some cases the vectors cross one another, but this, too, is nothing to cause concern.

Example: Solve for *R*, and the angle it makes with the *X*-axis.

Note that in solution *A* in Figure 11–34 we began with the 120-lb$_f$ component

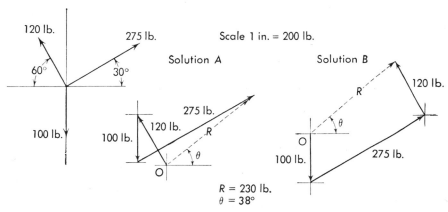

Figure 11–34.

and used components in a counterclockwise direction, while in solution *B* we began with the 100-lb$_f$ component and worked in a counterclockwise direction.

Problems

Solve, using the polygon of forces. Find the resultant of each of the following force systems and the angle the resultant makes with force *A*.

11–64. Forces *A* and *B* act 136° apart. $A = 180$ lb$_f$, $B = 325$ lb$_f$.

11–65. Forces *A* and *B* act 21° apart. $A = 39.3$ lb$_f$, $B = 41.6$ lb$_f$.

11–66. Forces *A*, *B*, and *C* act 49° apart, with *B* acting between *A* and *C*. $A = 49.3$ lb$_f$, $B = 66.7$ lb$_f$, $C = 35.8$ lb$_f$.

11–67. Find the resultant force which would replace the three forces in Figure 11–35.

11–68. A man weighing 210 lb$_f$ stands at the middle of a wire supported at points 60 ft apart and depresses it 12 ft below the level of the ends. Solve for the tension in the wire due to the man's weight.

11–69. Solve for the magnitude and direction of the resultant of the forces shown in Figure 11–36.

11–70. Find the resultant force that would replace the three forces *A*, *B*, and *C* in Figure 11–37.

11–71. Find the resultant of the four forces shown in Figure 11–38.

11–72. Solve for the resultant of the force systems shown in Figure 11–39.

11–73. Graphically resolve the force, shown in Figure 11–40 into three components, one of which is 10 lb$_f$ acting vertically upward and another 30 lb$_f$ acting horizontally to the left.

Problems (continued)

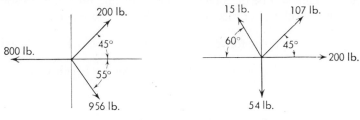

Figure 11–35.   Figure 11–36.

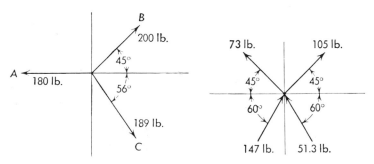

Figure 11–37.   Figure 11–38.

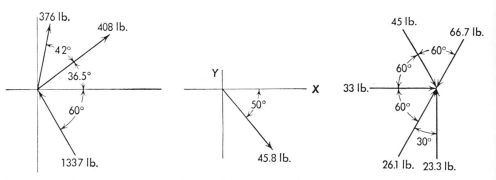

Figure 11–39.   Figure 11–40.   Figure 11–41.

11–74. Find the resultant of the force system shown in Figure 11–41, using a scale of 1 in. equals 10 lb$_f$.

11–75. Find the resultant of the velocity vectors: 33 mph south, 75 fps 20° west of north, and 2530 fpm north.

Rectangular Components

Graphical solutions, such as the *parallelogram method* and the *polygon of forces,* are useful for estimations where time is a factor. However, where exactitude is important, a numerical technique is needed. The method most frequently used by engineers is the *rectangular component method,* which will be discussed here.

As we have seen in the previous methods, vector components can be added together or subtracted—always leaving some resultant value. (This resultant value, of course, may be zero.) Also, any vector or resultant value can be replaced by two or more other vectors that are usually called *components.* If the components are two in number and perpendicular to each other, they are called *rectangular components.* Although it is common practice to use space coordinate axes that are horizontal and vertical, it is by no means necessary to do so. Any orientation of the axes will produce equivalent results.

Figure 11–42 shows a vector quantity F and its rectangular components F_x and F_y. Note that the lengths of the components F_x and F_y can be determined numerically by trigonometry. The components F_x and F_y also can be resolved into the force F by the polygon of forces. Hence, they may replace the force F in any computation.

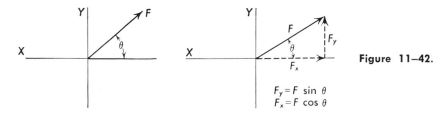

$$F_y = F \sin \theta$$
$$F_x = F \cos \theta$$

Figure 11–42.

Example: Let us examine a concurrent coplanar force system and resolve each force into its rectangular components (see Figure 11–43). By trigonometry, F_x can be found, using F and the cosine of the angle θ, or $F_x = F \cos \theta°$. In the same manner $F_y = F \sin \theta°$.

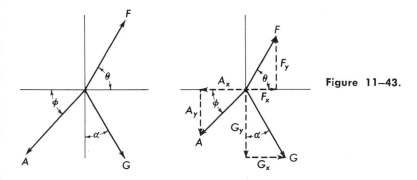

Figure 11–43.

In order to keep the directions of the vectors better in mind, let us assume that horizontal forces acting to the right are positive and those acting to the left are negative. Also, the forces acting upward may be considered positive and those acting downward negative.

In working such force systems by solving for the rectangular components, a table may be used. When the sums of the horizontal and vertical components have been determined, lay off these values on a new pair of axes to prevent confusion. Solve for the resultant in both magnitude and direction, using the method explained on page 44.

Example: Solve for R in Figure 11–44, using the method of rectangular components (see Figure 11–45 for the final resolution of the force system).

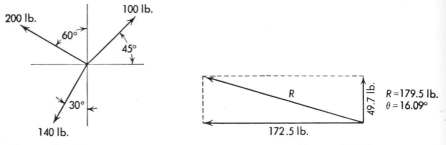

Figure 11–44.

Figure 11–45.

FORCES	HORIZONTAL COMPONENT	HORIZONTAL VALUE	VERTICAL COMPONENT	VERTICAL VALUE
$100 \ lb_f$	$100 \cos 45°$ =	$+70.7 \ lb_f$	$100 \sin 45°$ =	$+70.7 \ lb_f$
$200 \ lb_f$	$200 \sin 60°$ =	$-173.2 \ lb_f$	$200 \cos 60°$ =	$+100 \ lb_f$
$140 \ lb_f$	$140 \sin 30°$ =	$-70.0 \ lb_f$	$140 \cos 30°$ =	$-121 \ lb_f$
Total value	Positive	$+70.7 \ lb_f$	Positive	$+170.7 \ lb_f$
Total value	Negative	$-243.2 \ lb_f$	Negative	$-121 \ lb_f$
Sum	Horizontal	$-172.5 \ lb_f$	Vertical	$+49.7 \ lb_f$

Problems

Solve, using rectangular components (analytical method).

11–76. Find the resultant, in amount and direction, of the following concurrent coplanar force system: force A, 180 lb_f acts S 60° W; and force B, 158 lb_f, acts S 80° W. Check graphically, using a scale of 1 in. equals 50 lb_f.

11–77. Find the resultant of the following concurrent coplanar force system: $A = 30 \ lb_f$ due north; $B = 25 \ lb_f$ N 30° E; $C = 35 \ lb_f$ S 45° E; $D = 55 \ lb_f$ S 30° W.

11–78. Four men are pulling a box. A pulls with a force of 115 lb_f, N 20°40′ E; B pulls with a force of 95 lb_f S 64°35′ E; C pulls with a force of 140 lb_f N 40°20′ E; and D pulls with a force of 68 lb_f E. In what direction will the box tend to move?

11–79. Determine the amount and direction of the resultant of the concurrent coplanar force system as follows: force A, 10 lb_f, acting N 55° E; force B, 16 lb_f, acting due east; force C, 12 lb_f, acting S 22° W; force D, 15 lb_f, acting due west; force E, 17 lb_f, acting N 10° W.

11–80. Find the resultant and the angle the resultant makes with the vertical, using the following data: 10 lb_f, N 18° W; 5 lb_f, N 75° E; 3 lb_f, S 64° E; 7 lb_f, S 0° W; 10 lb_f, S 50° W.

11–81. Five forces act on an object. The forces are as follows: 130 lb$_f$, 0°; 170 lb$_f$, 90°; 70 lb$_f$, 180°; 20 lb$_f$, 270°; 300 lb$_f$, 150°. The angles are measured counterclockwise with reference to the horizontal through the origin. Determine graphically the amount and direction of the resultant by means of the polygon of forces. Check analytically, using horizontal and vertical components. Calculate the angle that R makes with the horizontal.

11–82. (*a*) In the sketch in Figure 11–46, using rectangular components, find the resultant of these four forces: $A = 100$ lb$_f$, $B = 130$ lb$_f$, $C = 195$ lb$_f$, $D = 138$ lb$_f$. (*b*) Find a resultant force that would replace forces A and B. (*c*) By the polygon of forces, break force A into two components, one of which acts N 10° E and has a magnitude of 65 lb$_f$. Give the magnitude and direction of the second component.

11–83. Two inclined posts, making angles of 45° and 60° with the horizontal, are pinned together 8 ft above the ground. If a load of 1800 lb$_f$ is hung from the pin, solve for the compression forces in the posts.

11–84. A weight of 1200 lb$_f$ is hung by a cable 23 ft long. What horizontal pull will be necessary to hold the weight 8 ft from a vertical line through the point of support? What will be the tension in the cable?

11–85. A weight of 80 lb$_f$ is suspended by two cords, the tension in AC being 70 lb$_f$ and in BC being 25 lb$_f$, as shown in Figure 11–47. Find the angles α and θ.

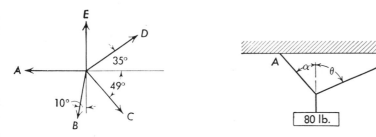

Figure 11–46.   Figure 11–47.

MOMENTS

If a force is applied perpendicular to a pivoted beam at some distance away from the pivot point, there will be a tendency to cause the beam to turn in either a clockwise or counterclockwise direction (see Figure 11–48). The direction of the tendency will depend on the direction of the applied force. This tendency of a force to cause rotation about a given center is called *moment* (see Figure 11–49).

The amount of *moment* will depend upon the magnitude of the applied force as well as upon the length of the moment arm. The moment arm is the perpendicular distance from the point of rotation to the applied force. The magnitude of the moment is calculated by multiplying the force by the moment arm.

The sign convention being used in a given problem analysis should be placed on the calculation sheet adjacent to the problem sketch. In this way no confusion will arise in the mind of the reader concerning the sign convention being used. We shall

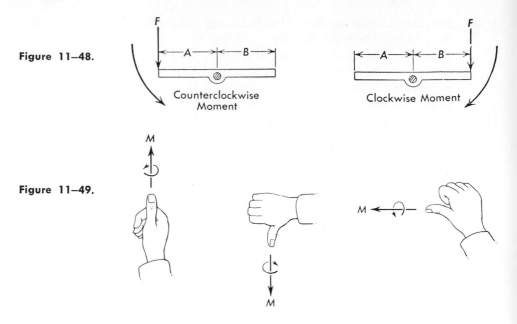

Figure 11–48.

Counterclockwise Moment

Clockwise Moment

Figure 11–49.

assume that vectors acting to the right have a positive sign, vectors acting upward have a positive sign, and moments directed counterclockwise have a positive sign. To aid in establishing a system of positive senses, the sketch shown in Figure 11–50 will serve as a basis for problem analysis in this text.

Example:

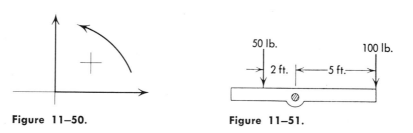

Figure 11–50.

Figure 11–51.

Example: Solve for the moments in Figure 11–51 that tend to cause turning of the beam about the axle.

$$\text{Counterclockwise moment} = (\ 50 \text{ lb}) \ (2 \text{ ft}) = +100 \text{ lb-ft}$$
$$\text{Clockwise moment} = (100 \text{ lb}) \ (5 \text{ ft}) = -500 \text{ lb-ft}$$

Since *moment* is the product of a force and a distance, its units will be the product of force and length units. By convention, moments are usually expressed with the force unit being shown first, as $\text{lb}_f\text{-ft}$, $\text{lb}_f\text{-in.}$, kip-ft (a kip is 1000 lb_f), etc. This is done because *work* and *energy* also involve the product of distance and force, and the units ft-lb_f, in-lb_f, etc., are commonly used for this purpose.

The moment of a force about some given center is identical to the sum of the moments of the components of the force about the same center. This principle is commonly called *Varignon's theorem*. In problem analysis it is sometimes more convenient to solve for the sum of the moments of the components of a force rather than the moment of the force itself. However, the problem solutions will be identical.

Example: Solve for the total moment of the 1000-lb$_f$ force about point A in Figure 11–52.

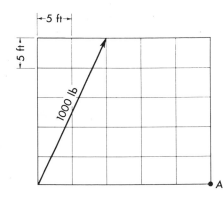

Figure 11–52.

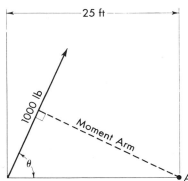

Figure 11–53.   Figure 11–54. Moments of components of a force.

SOLUTION A: Moment of a force as shown in Figure 11–53.
$$\theta = \text{arc tan } 25/10 = 68.2°$$
$$\text{Moment arm} = 25 \sin 68.2°$$
$$\text{Total moment} = (1000)\,(25 \sin 68.2°)$$
$$= 23,200 \text{ lb}_f\text{-ft}$$

SOLUTION B: Moments of components of a force as shown in Figure 11–54.
$$\text{Vertical component} = 1000 \sin 68.2°$$
and $$\text{Moment arm} = 25 \text{ ft}$$
$$\text{Horizontal component} = 1000 \cos 68.2°$$
and $$\text{Moment arm} = 0$$

(Note that the horizontal component passes through the center A.)
$$\text{Total moment} = (1000 \sin 68.2°)\,(25) = 23,200 \text{ lb}_f\text{-ft}$$

Problems

11–86. Solve for the algebraic sum of the moments in pound-feet about A when h is 20 in. as shown in Figure 11–55.

11–87. Solve for the algebraic sum of the moments of forces about A in Figure 11–56.

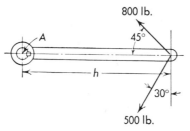

Figure 11–55.

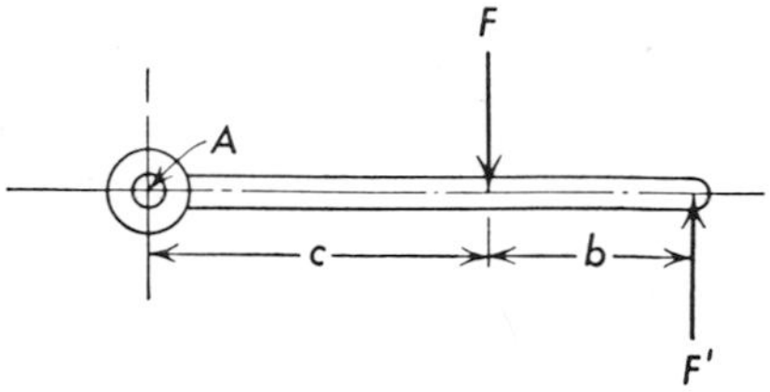

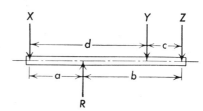

Figure 11–56.

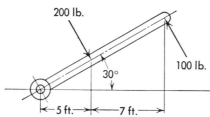

Figure 11–57.

Figure 11–58.

11–88. Solve for the algebraic sum of the moments about the center of the axle shown in Figure 11–57.

11–89. (*a*) Write an equation for the clockwise moments about the point of application of force R in Figure 11–58. (*b*) Write an equation for the counterclockwise moments about the point of application of force Y.

11–90. (*a*) Solve for the clockwise moments about A, B, C, D, and E in Figure 11–59. (*b*) Solve for the counterclockwise moments about A, B, C, D, and E. (*c*) Solve for the algebraic sum of the moments about A, B, C, D, and E.

11–91. Find the summation of the moments of the forces shown around A in Figure 11–60. Find the moment sum around D.

11–92. Find the moment of each of the forces shown about O in Figure 11–61.

11–93. What pull P is required on the handle of a claw hammer to exert a vertical force of 750 lb$_f$ on a nail. Dimensions are shown on Figure 11–62.

11–94. On the trapezoidal body shown in Figure 11–63 find the moment of each of the forces about point O.

11–95. Find the moment of each of the forces shown in Figure 11–64 about the point A.

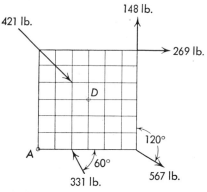

Figure 11–60.

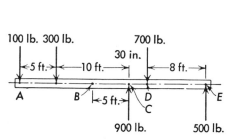

Figure 11–59.

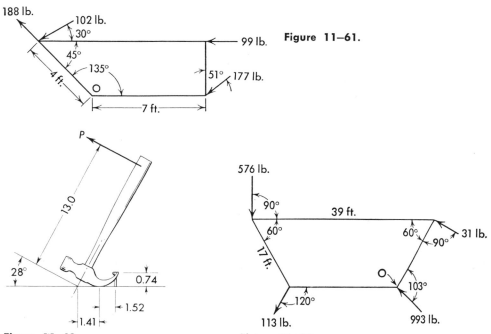

Figure 11–61.

Figure 11–62.

Figure 11–63.

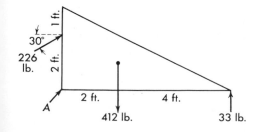

Figure 11–64.

EQUILIBRIUM

The term *equilibrium* is used to describe the condition of any body when the resultant of all forces acting on the body equals zero. For example, the forces acting upward on a body in equilibrium must be balanced by other forces acting downward on the body. Also, the forces acting horizontally to the right are counteracted by equal forces acting horizontally to the left. Since no unbalance in moment or turning effect can be present when a body is in equilibrium, the sum of the moments of all forces acting on the body must also be zero. The moment center may be located at any convenient place on the body or at any place in space. We may sum up these conditions of equilibrium by the following equations:

$\Sigma F_x = 0$ (the sum of all horizontal forces acting on the body equals zero)
$\Sigma F_y = 0$ (the sum of all vertical forces acting on the body equals zero)
$\Sigma M_o = 0$ (the sum of the moments of all forces acting on the body equals zero)

These equilibrium equations may be used to good advantage in working problems involving beams, trusses, and levers.

Example: A beam of negligible weight is supported at each end by a knife-edge. The beam carries a concentrated load of 500 lb$_f$ and one uniformly distributed load weighing 100 lb$_f$ per linear foot, as shown in Figure 11–65. Determine the scale readings under the knife-edges.

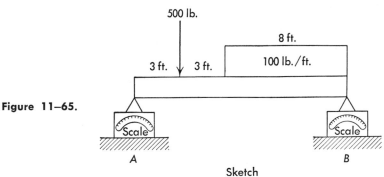

Figure 11–65.

SOLUTION: The uniformly distributed load is equivalent to a resultant of 8 ft $\times$ 100 lb$_f$/ft $=$ 800 lb$_f$ acting at the center of gravity of the uniform-load diagram. Therefore the entire distribution load can be replaced by a concentrated load of 800 lb$_f$ acting at a distance of 10 ft from the left end as shown in Figure 11–66.

1. Draw a free-body diagram of the beam.
2. Since there are no horizontal forces acting on the free body, $\Sigma F_x = 0$ is satisfied.
3. From $\Sigma F_y = 0$, we know that

$$A + B = 500 \text{ lb}_f + 800 \text{ lb}_f$$
$$A + B = 1300 \text{ lb}_f$$

4. From $\Sigma M_o = 0$, we know that the moments about any point must equal zero. Let us take moments about point A.

$$\Sigma M_A = 0$$
$$(B \text{ lb}_f)(14 \text{ ft}) - (500 \text{ lb}_f)(3 \text{ ft}) - (800 \text{ lb}_f)(10 \text{ ft}) = 0$$
$$B \text{ lb}_f = \frac{1500 \text{ lb}_f\text{-ft} + 8000 \text{ lb}_f\text{-ft}}{14 \text{ ft}}$$
$$B \text{ lb}_f = \frac{9500 \text{ lb}_f\text{-ft}}{14 \text{ ft}}$$
$$B = 679 \text{ lb}_f$$

5. From the third step we saw that $A + B = 1300$ lb$_f$. We can now subtract and obtain

$$A = 1300 \text{ lb}_f - 679 \text{ lb}_f = 621 \text{ lb}_f$$

NOTE: The same answer for A could have been obtained by taking moments about B as a moment center.

In this book problems involving trusses, cranes, linkages, bridges, etc., should

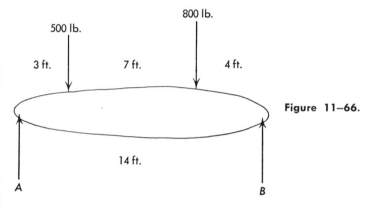

Figure 11–66.

be considered to be *pin-connected,* which means that the member is free to rotate about the joint. For simplicity, members also are usually considered to be weightless.

By examining each member of the structure separately, internal forces in the various members may be obtained by the conditions of equilibrium.

Example: Solve for the tensions in cables AF and ED and for the reactions at C and R in Figure 11–67.

Equilibrium Equations

$$\Sigma F_x = 0$$
$$\Sigma F_y = 0$$
$$\Sigma M_o = 0$$

SOLUTION

1. Take moments about point R in free body No. 1, (see Figure 11–68).

$$\Sigma M_R = 0$$
$$(12 \text{ ft})(FA) - (100 \text{ lb}_f)(4 \text{ ft}) = 0$$

$$FA = \frac{400 \text{ lb}_f\text{-ft}}{12 \text{ ft}} = 33.3 \text{ lb}_f$$

$$\Sigma F_x = 0$$
$$R_x - FA = 0$$
$$R_x = FA = 33.3 \text{ lb}_f \rightarrow$$

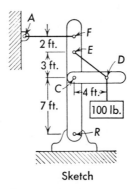

Sketch

Figure 11–67.

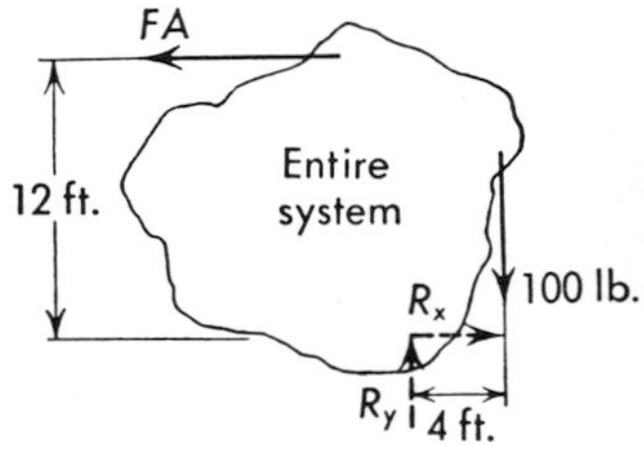

Free Body #1

Figure 11–68.

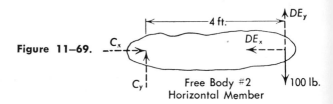

Figure 11–69.

Free Body #2
Horizontal Member

2. Take moments about point C in free body No. 2, (see Figure 11–69).

$$\Sigma M_c = DE_y (4) - 100 (4) = 0$$
$$DE_y = 100 \text{ lb}_f$$

Therefore
$$DE = \frac{100 \text{ lb}_f}{\sin 36.9°} = 166.8 \text{ lb}_f \searrow$$

And free body No. 2

$$\Sigma F_y = 0$$
$$C_y = 100 \text{ lb}_f - 100 \text{ lb}_f$$
$$C_y = 0$$

Also free body No. 2

$$\Sigma F_x = 0$$
$$C_x = DE_x = \frac{100 \text{ lb}_f}{\tan 36.9°}$$
$$C_x = 133.1 \text{ lb}_f \rightarrow$$

3. Consider $\Sigma F_y = 0$, using the third free body (vertical member) as shown in Figure 11–70. Remember that in two force members, such as cable DE, the reactions at each end will be equal in magnitude but opposite in direction; that is, E_x and E_y are equal to DE_x and DE_y.

$$\Sigma F_y = 0$$
$$R_y - DE_y = 0$$
$$R_y = 100.0 \text{ lb}_f \uparrow$$

The resultant is indicated as before and solved by using the slide rule (see Figure 11–71.

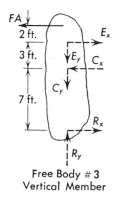

Free Body #3
Vertical Member

Figure 11–70.

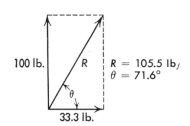

100 lb. R   R = 105.5 lb$_f$
              $\theta = 71.6°$

33.3 lb.

Figure 11–71.

Equilibrium Problems

11–96. A horizontal beam 20 ft long weighs 150 lb$_f$. It is supported at the left end and 4 ft from the right end. It has the following concentrated loads: at the left end, 200 lb$_f$; 8 ft from the left end, 300 lb$_f$; at the right end, 400 lb$_f$. Calculate the reactions at the supports.

11–97. A horizontal beam 8 ft long and weighing 30 lb$_f$ is supported at the left end and 2 ft from the right end. It has the following loads: at the left end, 18 lb$_f$; 3 ft from the left end, 22 lb$_f$; at the right end, 15 lb$_f$. Compute the reactions at the supports.

11–98. A beam 22 ft long weighing 300 lb$_f$ is supporting loads of 700 lb$_f$ 3 ft from the left end and 250 lb$_f$ 7 ft from the right end. One support is at the left end. How far from the right end should the right support be placed so that the reactions at the two supports will be equal?

11–99. A beam 18 ft long is supported at the right end and at a point 5 ft from the left end. It is loaded with a concentrated load of 250 lb$_f$ located 2 ft from the right end and a concentrated load of 450 lb$_f$ located 9 ft from the right end. In addition, it has a uniform load of 20 lb$_f$ per linear foot for its entire length. Find the reactions at the supports.

11–100. A 12-ft beam which weighs 10 lb$_f$ per foot is resting horizontally. The left end of the beam is pinned to a vertical wall. The right end of the beam is supported by a cable that is attached to the vertical wall 6 ft above the left end of the beam. There is a 200-lb$_f$ concentrated load acting vertically

Equilibrium Problems (continued)

downward 3 ft from the right end of the beam. Determine the tension in the cable and the amount and direction of the reaction at the left end of the beam.

11–101. A steel I-beam, weighing 75 lb_f per linear foot and 20 ft long, is supported at its left end and at a point 4 ft from its right end. It carries loads of 10 tons and 6 tons at distances of 5 ft and 17 ft, respectively, from the left end. Find the reactions at the supports.

11–102. A horizontal rod 8 ft long and weighing 12 lb_f has a weight of 15 lb_f hung from the right end, and a weight of 4 lb_f hung from the left end. Where should a single support be located so the rod will balance?

11–103. A uniform board 22 ft long will balance 4.2 ft from one end when a weight of 61 lb_f is hung from this end. How much does the board weigh?

11–104. An iron beam 12.7 ft long weighing 855 lb_f has a load of 229 lb_f at the right end. A support is located 7.2 ft from the load end. (*a*) How much force is required at the opposite end to balance it? (*b*) Disregarding the balancing force, calculate the reactions on the supports if one support is located 7 ft from the left end and the other support is located 4 ft from the right end.

11–105. A horizontal rod 8 ft long and weighing 1.2 lb_f per linear foot has a weight of 15 lb_f hung from the right end, and a weight of 4 lb_f hung from the left end. Where should a single support be located so the rod will balance?

11–106. A 2-ft diameter sphere weighs 56 lb_f, is suspended by a cable, and rests against a vertical wall. If the cable AB is 2 ft long, (*a*) calculate the angle the cable will make with the smooth wall, (*b*) solve for the tension in the cable and the reaction at C in Figure 11–72. Check results graphically.

11–107. What horizontal pull P will be necessary just to start the wheel weighing 1400 lb_f over the 4-in. block in Figure 11–73?

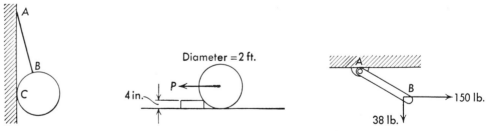

Figure 11–72.   Figure 11–73.   Figure 11–74.

11–108. A vertical pole 12 ft long is pinned to the ground at A and is stayed by a guy wire running from the top of the pole, B, to a point C, 8 ft to the left of A. If a horizontal force of 1900 lb_f is applied to the pole at D, 6 ft above A, determine the tension in the guy wire BC, and the amount and direction of the pin reaction at A.

11–109. Find the tension in AB and the angle θ that AB makes with the vertical in Figure 11–74.

11–110. If the tension in the cable AB in Figure 11–75, is 196 lb$_f$, how much does the sphere B weigh? How much is the reaction of the inclined plane on the sphere?

11–111. The wheel B in Figure 11–76 weighs 175 lb$_f$. Solve for the force in member AB, the reaction at C, and the horizontal and vertical force components at A.

11–112. A cylinder weighing 206 lb$_f$ is placed in a smooth trough as shown in Figure 11–77. Find the two supporting forces.

11–113. A 796-lb$_f$ load is supported as shown in Figure 11–78. AB equals 8 ft, θ equals 25°. (*a*) Neglecting the weight of the beam AB, solve analytically for the tension in the cable and the reaction at A. (*b*) If beam AB is uniform and weighs 12 lb$_f$ per foot, solve for the tension in the cable and the reaction at A.

11–114. Find the tension in AB and the compression in BC in Figure 11–79.

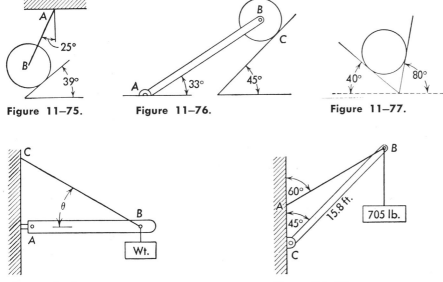

Figure 11–75.   Figure 11–76.   Figure 11–77.

Figure 11–78.   Figure 11–79.

11–115. A weight of 1355 lb$_f$ is supported by two ropes making angles of 30° and 45° on opposite sides of the vertical. What is the tension in each rope?

11–116. Forces are applied on a rigid frame as shown in Figure 11–80. Find the reactions at A and B.

11–117. (*a*) What is the tension in BC in Figure 11–81? (*b*) What is the amount and direction of the reaction at A?

11–118. (*a*) Find the tension in AC in Figure 11–82. (*b*) Find the amount and direction of the reaction at B. $BC = 10$ ft, $BD = 25$ ft.

11–119. Cylinder No. 1 in Figure 11–83 has a 10-in. diameter and weighs 84 lb$_f$. Cylinder No. 2 has a 6-in. diameter and weighs 27 lb$_f$. Find the reactions at A, B, and C. All surfaces are smooth.

Equilibrium Problems (continued)

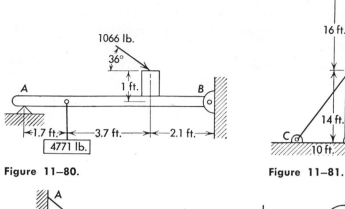

Figure 11–80.

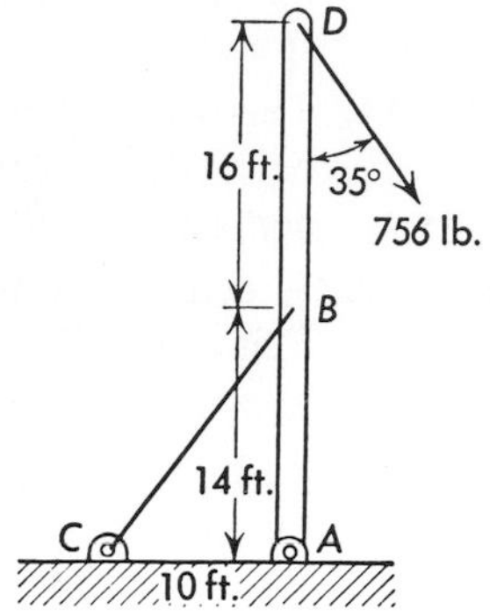

Figure 11–81.

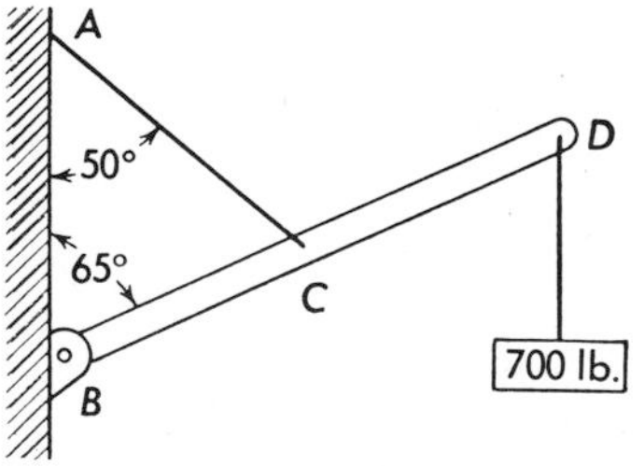

Figure 11–82.

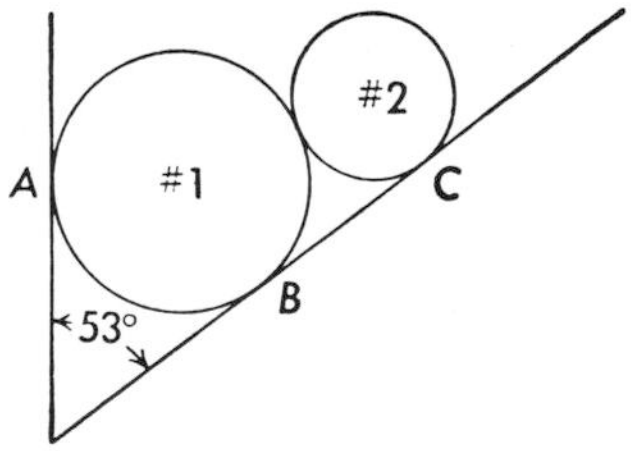

Figure 11–83.

11–120. (*a*) Find the force in member *AB* in Figure 11–84 and the reaction at point *E*. (*b*) Find the force in member *CG* and the horizontal and vertical components of the reaction at pin *D*.

11–121. Solve for the reactions at 1, 2, 3, 4, and 5 in Figure 11–85. Weights: $A = 150$ lb$_f$, $B = 100$ lb$_f$, $C = 70$ lb$_f$, $D = 35$ lb$_f$. Diameters: $A = 26$ in., $B = 20$ in., $C = 15$ in., $D = 9$ in. Angle $\theta = 30°$.

11–122. A 15-ft ladder leans against the side of a smooth building in such a position that it makes an angle of 60° with the ground (horizontal). A man weighing 190 lb$_f$ stands on the ladder three-fourths of the way up the ladder. The bottom of the ladder is prevented from sliding by the

Figure 11–84.

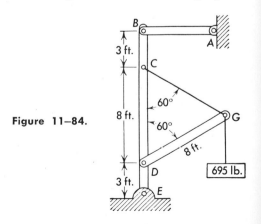

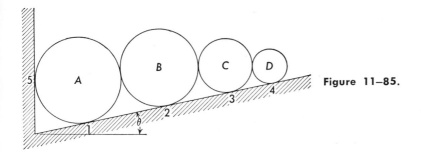

Figure 11–85.

ground. Find the horizontal and vertical components of the reaction at the foot of the ladder and the force between the ladder and the wall.

ELECTRICITY AND ELECTRONICS

The use of electrical machinery and electronic devices has become so much a part of our present day life that practically all engineers will work with electricity in some way in their professional role. The applications of electrical phenomena are so widespread that all engineering students should have some basic knowledge of the principles of electricity.

Although the knowledge of electrostatic and magnetic effects has been available for many centuries, the concept that there was any relation between electric charge effects and magnetic effects was not presented until the last century. An English mathematician, Clerk Maxwell, was the individual principally responsible for providing a mathematical basis for showing a relationship between electricity and magnetism. His mathematical derivations were based on experimental work done previously by such scientists as Ampere, Volta, Faraday, and Coulomb.

Although we can look back and consider with disdain the difficulties of early experimenters in performing what to us are the most elementary demonstrations of electrical and magnetic phenomena, we must remember that in the days of early experimenters, no one knew even the difference between insulators and conductors. The discovery of the insulating properties of certain materials provided a means for isolating charges and directing their flow. This one discovery, which to us is almost an intuitive concept, was to the early experimenters a major breakthrough in their work. Could it be that fifty years from now, engineers will look back at our present difficulties in grasping concepts of solid-state electronic devices and wonder why we made such a task of attempting to understand the behavior of such obviously elementary phenomena?

The Atom

The basis for explaining the behavior of electricity depends on our concept of the atomic structure of matter. As any student of science knows, within the atom is a system of electrons in orbit surrounding a central nucleus. Some of these electrons in the outer orbit can be transferred to other atoms under the influence of such phenomena as electrical fields, heat, friction, and so on.

Materials differ widely in their tendency to transfer electrons, and all materials can be classified broadly into insulators or conductors as a measure of the ease with which electrons are transferred. For example, if hard rubber is stroked with a woolen cloth, friction will transfer electrons from the cloth to the hard rubber but, since the hard rubber atoms cling tightly to the electrons, little or no movement of the charges can then occur on the surface of the hard rubber.

On the other hand, if a piece of copper is charged, the charges will move readily through the copper by transfer from atom to atom, and, unless insulating structures are provided, the charges usually will dissipate rapidly to other conducting mediums.

The concept of conductors or insulators then deals not with the production of electrical charges but rather with the relative ease with which charges are transferred.

Since the electrons appear to be moving in orbits, each electron will tend to produce a magnetic field due to its own motion. In almost every material, the orientation of the spins is such that the magnetic effects cancel and the resultant field is substantially zero. However, in the case of iron, nickel, and cobalt, together with a few alloys, the magnetic fields due to the electron spins do not cancel and the atom or molecule does have a definite magnetic pattern. In simplified terms, this is the general concept of the relation between electrical and magnetic effects.

In a classical experiment conducted by Professor Millikan early in the century, the numerical value of the charge on an electron was measured. As a result of this measurement, we find that the number of electrons flowing through the filament of an ordinary 100-watt 110-volt electric light bulb is approximately 6.28×10^{18} electrons per second.

Electrostatic generators are used to separate charges in the production of very penetrating x-rays and in research on the acceleration of charged particles. A Van de Graff generator is an example of a static charge generator. With this type of machine, potentials of several million volts can be secured.

Another example of charges being produced by external forces is in the case of piezoelectricity. It has been determined experimentally that certain crystalline substances such as quartz and Rochelle salts will have a separation of charges produced by mechanical deformation of the crystal. Electronic devices can sense this charged condition of certain faces of the crystal and by amplification of the charge effects can convert them to many useful purposes. A microphone, for example, can be made by having sound waves strike a flexible diaphragm that in turn is coupled mechanically to a crystal. The deflections of the crystal will produce in electrical charges corresponding charges that when amplified can be heard in a loudspeaker.

Electric Currents

If charged particles, usually electrons, move in a conductor, the movement of the charges constitutes what is known as an electric current. Obviously the charges will not move unless there is an excess of charges at one point and a deficiency at another. In the case of a simple electric cell, the tendency of one of the electrode materials to be chemically changed results in an ionization process that will produce a difference in charges on the electrodes. As long as an external path of conducting material exists, the charges flow from one electrode to another in an attempt to equalize the charges. A coulomb is approximately 6.28×10^{18} electrons and a flow of 1 coulomb per second past a given point in an electrical circuit is defined as a current of 1 ampere.

Voltage basically is a measure of the amount of work or energy necessary to move a certain number of charges from one place to another against opposition. A voltage can be present even though the charges actually are not moving. For example, in a certain storage battery, a voltage, representing a state of separation of charges within the battery, exists regardless of whether the circuit is completed so that current can flow. This can be compared to having a pile of rocks on a platform. Potential energy due to the rock's elevated position is present even though the rocks are not moving. The usual unit of voltage is the volt—the voltage necessary to move one ampere through an opposition of 1 ohm of resistance.

Resistance of flow of an electric current exists because of the difficulty of moving electrons from one atom to another. All materials have some resistance to current flow except that certain metals at temperatures near absolute zero temperature (approximately −459°F), appear to have negligible resistance. Commonly used materials having quite low resistances at ordinary temperatures are silver, copper, and aluminum. All metals are good conductors; however, the three mentioned are the best conducting materials. Other substances having relatively low resistance are carbon and solutions containing ions. Almost without exception, all other materials are insulators having resistances from thousands to millions of times that of the metals. In some cases, insulators at ordinary temperatures will become fairly good conductors at temperatures of several hundred degrees and upward. Glass and some plastics possess this property of having a markedly lower resistance at elevated temperatures. As mentioned above, the unit of resistance is the ohm and is defined legally as the resistance of a column of mercury 1 sq mm in cross section and 106.3 cm long held at a temperature of 0°C.

Laws and Principles

A well known relation of electrical quantities in a circuit is called Ohm's Law. Stated briefly, it says that in a circuit, the ratio of the voltage to the current is a constant. Of course, like many laws, it must have limiting conditions, the major one being that the temperature of the conductor must remain constant. In symbol form:

$$\frac{V \text{ (voltage)}}{I \text{ (current)}} = R \text{ (resistance)}$$

This means that in a circuit of fixed resistance, if the voltage of the circuit is doubled, the current (flow) will also double.

There are two basic ways in which circuit elements can be connected. These are series and parallel connections. Examples are given in Figure 11–86.

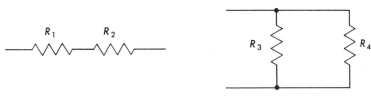

(a) An example of resistances connected in series

(b) An example of resistances connected in parallel

Figure 11–86. Two basic ways in which resistances can be connected.

Series Circuit

As an example of an application of Ohm's Law, if a simple series circuit is sketched showing a cell and a resistance with a cell voltage of 28.3 v and a resistance of 2.10 ohms, the current can be computed readily:

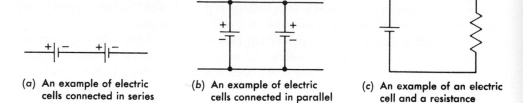

(a) An example of electric cells connected in series

(b) An example of electric cells connected in parallel

(c) An example of an electric cell and a resistance connected in series

Figure 11–87. Series and parallel arrangements of circuit elements.

Example: First, draw a simple sketch using conventional symbols and label the known quantities. Second, solve for the unknown quantities.

Figure 11–88. A simple series circuit using Ohm's Law for solution to obtain unknowns.

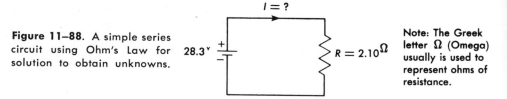

Note: The Greek letter Ω (Omega) usually is used to represent ohms of resistance.

Applying Ohm's Law

$$\frac{V}{I} = R$$

$$I = \frac{V \text{ (volts)}}{R \text{ (ohms)}}$$

$$I = \frac{28.3}{2.10} = 13.48 \text{ amp}$$

Since this is a closed circuit with no branches, the same current (13.48 amp) is flowing in all parts of the circuit, since it would be unlikely that charges would

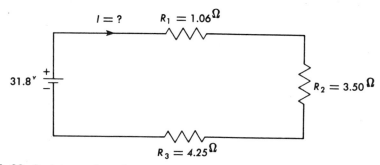

Figure 11–89. Resistances in series.

stack up at some given point. Also, the voltage produced by the cell is assumed to be all used in forcing the current through the resistance. This assumes that the resistance of the cell and of the connecting wires is negligible.

For another example, let us take a circuit where several resistances are connected in series as shown in Figure 11–89.

For this type of circuit, first add all the resistances to get a sum which is the equivalent of all the resistances together. This sum is 8.81 ohms. Then applying Ohm's Law:

$$I = \frac{V \text{ (volts)}}{R \text{ (ohms)}}$$

$$I = \frac{31.8}{8.81} = 3.61 \text{ amp}$$

Since the circuit elements are all in series, this same current flows through each element. At this time, we can compute the voltage across each resistance since a part of the total available voltage is used for each.

For Resistance R_1
$$V_1 = IR_1 \text{ volt}$$
$$V_1 = (3.61)(1.06) = 3.77 \text{ v}$$

For Resistance R_2
$$V_2 = (3.61)(3.50) = 12.64 \text{ v}$$

For Resistance R_3
$$V_3 = (3.61)(4.25) = 15.34 \text{ v}$$

As a check, the sum of the individual voltages across the resistances, frequently called the voltage drop across the resistance, can be obtained and should be the same as the original cell voltage, within slide rule accuracy.

$$V_1 + V_2 + V_3 = 31.75 \text{ v}$$

Parallel Circuits

Figure 11–90 is a sketch of a circuit containing resistances in parallel with the group connected in series with a cell.

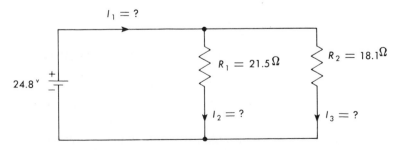

Figure 11–90. A parallel arrangement of resistances.

To solve for the currents in this circuit, first find the value of a single equivalent resistance that can replace the parallel set. This single equivalent can be found by the expression:

$$\frac{1}{R_{\text{equiv}}} = \frac{1}{R_1} + \frac{1}{R_2}$$

or

$$R_{\text{equiv}} = \frac{1}{\dfrac{1}{R_1} + \dfrac{1}{R_2}}$$

$$R_{\text{equiv}} = \frac{1}{\dfrac{1}{21.5} + \dfrac{1}{18.1}} = \frac{1}{0.0466 + 0.0553}$$

$$= \frac{1}{0.1019} = 9.83 \text{ ohm}$$

Using this equivalent resistance:

$$I_1 = \frac{V}{R_{\text{equiv}}}$$

$$I_1 = \frac{24.8}{9.83} = 2.52 \text{ amp}$$

Currents I_2 and I_3 can be found in several ways. For instance, since the currents will divide in inverse ratio to the resistances, a current ratio can be determined, and since the total current (2.52 amp) is known, the individual currents can be found. A more universal method is to find the current in each resistance by using the *voltage drop* method. Since, in a parallel circuit, the same voltage appears across each resistance, an application of Ohm's Law to each branch will permit a solution for the current.

$$I_2 = \frac{V}{R_1}$$

$$I_2 = \frac{24.8}{21.5} = 1.152 \text{ amp}$$

and

$$I_3 = \frac{V}{R_2}$$

$$I_3 = \frac{24.8}{18.1} = 1.370 \text{ amp}$$

As a check, $I_2 + I_3$ should add to give the total current out of the cell

$$I_1 = I_2 + I_3$$
$$I_1 = 1.157 + 1.370 = 2.52 \text{ amp}$$

To summarize, for series circuits, the current in all parts is the same and the sum of the voltage drops across the resistances equals the available cell voltage. For parallel circuits, the voltage is the same across each parallel path, and the sum of the currents in each branch or path equals the total current supplied by the cell.

Series-Parallel Circuits

If a problem involving a series-parallel combination of circuit elements is given, an application of the principles shown above will provide a means of solution.

Example:

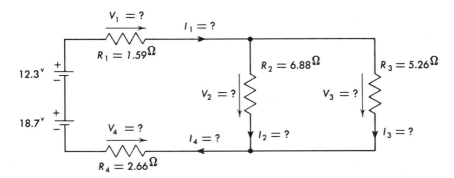

Figure 11–91. A series-parallel arrangement of resistances.

ANALYSIS: If the parallel arrangement of resistances R_2 and R_3 can be combined into a single equivalent resistance, the circuit then will be a single series circuit and a method of determining currents or voltages will be available as was used in a previous example.

SOLUTION: The equivalent resistance of R_2 and R_3 will be

$$\frac{1}{R_{\text{equiv}}} = \frac{1}{R_2} + \frac{1}{R_3}$$
$$\frac{1}{R_{\text{equiv}}} = \frac{1}{6.88} + \frac{1}{5.26}$$
$$= 0.1458 + 0.1902$$
$$= 0.3360$$

$$R_{\text{equiv}} = \frac{1}{0.3360} = 2.98 \text{ ohms}$$

This means that if the parallel combination were replaced by a single 2.98 ohm resistance, the current and voltage values in the remainder of the circuit would be unchanged. The circuit then can be redrawn substituting R_{equiv} for R_2 and R_3 as shown in Figure 11–92 on the next page.

First, obtain the total voltage of the electric cells. This is simply the sum of the individual cell voltages.

$$V_{\text{total}} = 12.3 + 18.7$$
$$= 31.0 \text{ v}$$

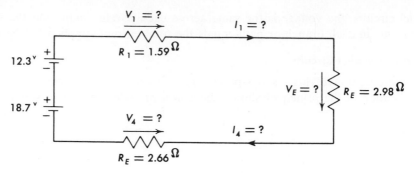

Figure 11–92. The equivalent circuit of Figure 11–91.

Second, find the total circuit resistance. For this circuit, it is the sum of the individual resistances in series.

$$R_{total} = 1.59 + 2.98 + 2.66$$
$$= 7.23 \text{ ohm}$$

Third, find the total circuit current. This is found by an application of Ohm's Law using total voltage and total resistance.

$$I_{total} = \frac{V_{total}}{R_{total}}$$

$$= \frac{31.0}{7.23} = 4.28 \text{ amp}$$

Since, in a series circuit, the total current is the same as the current in each part, the current through each resistance also is 4.28 amp. From this, we can obtain the voltage drop across each resistance by applying Ohm's Law only to that part of the circuit.

$$V_1 = I_1 R_1$$
$$= (4.28)(1.59) = 6.80 \text{ v}$$
$$V_E = I_1 R_E$$
$$= (4.28)(2.98) = 12.78 \text{ v}$$
$$V_4 = I_1 R_4$$
$$= (4.28)(2.66) = 11.42 \text{ v}$$

As a check, the sum of V_1, V_E, and V_4 should be the same as the available voltage from the cells.

Fourth, referring back to Figure 11–91, we now can solve for the currents I_2 and I_3. Since the voltage across the equivalent resistance was 12.78 v, this will also be the voltage across each member of the parallel set. That is:

$$V_E = V_2 = V_3 = 12.78 \text{ volt}$$

The current I_2 and I_3 can be found by applying Ohm's Law only to that part of the circuit.

$$I_2 = \frac{V_2}{R_2}$$
$$= \frac{12.78}{6.88} = 1.858 \text{ amp}$$

and
$$I_3 = \frac{12.78}{5.26} = 2.43 \text{ amp}$$

As a check, $I_2 + I_3$ should equal I_1 or I_4.

More complicated circuits involving delta-wye transformations, applications of Kirchhoff's laws, or network theorems are not discussed here. However, the student may wish to investigate these additional methods of circuit solutions.

Power

Electric power is determined in dc circuits by the product of current and voltage. That is

$$P = VI$$

where P is the power in watts, V is the voltage in volts, and I is the current in amperes. This expression can be applied to a part of a circuit, but then only the current and voltage in that part can be used.

Example: Refer to Figure 11–91. Suppose it is required to determine the power used in Resistance R_2 and the total power supplied by the battery.

For the resistance R_2 power, use values only for that part.

$$P_R = V_2 I_2 \text{ (v)(amp)}$$
$$P_R = (12.78)(1.858)$$
$$= 23.7 \text{ w}$$

For the battery power, use total voltage and current values.

$$P_B = V_B I_1$$
$$= (12.3 + 18.7)(4.28)$$
$$= 133 \text{ w}$$

By algebra it can be shown that power also can be found by these expressions:

$$P = \frac{V^2}{R} \frac{(\text{volts})^2}{\text{ohm}}$$
$$P = I^2 R$$

In alternating current circuits, power expressions must be modified to account for the possibility of the maximum value of current and the maximum value of voltage not occurring at the same time. This phenomena usually is referred to as the current leading the voltage or the current lagging the voltage and is caused by the presence of capacitive or inductive components in the circuit. A detailed explanation of these effects is beyond the scope of this discussion, but this leading or lagging effect is a function of time and usually is written as

$$P = VI \cos \theta$$

where P is the power in watts, V is the voltage in volts, I is the current in amperes, and θ is the angle called "phase angle" between a vector representing voltage and one representing current.

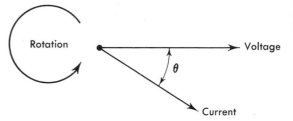

Figure 11–93. Vector representation of voltage and current in an alternating current circuit.

The diagram shown in Figure 11–93 is a vector system assumed to rotate counterclockwise, and it generates sinusoidal traces on a linear time base. This figure represents current lagging in time behind the voltage. This can be caused by the presence of an inductance, usually a coil producing a magnetic field, in the alternating current circuit.

In making alternating current power measurements in a circuit having an inductance, the product of a voltmeter reading and an ammeter reading will be different from the reading of a wattmeter by the factor, $\cos \theta$. Since the wattmeter reads power, the phase angle, θ, can be found from the meter readings by the expression:

$$\cos \theta = \frac{P_{\text{wattmeter}}}{(V_{\text{voltmeter}})(I_{\text{ammeter}})}$$

The expression $\cos \theta$ frequently is referred to as "power factor." It is possible to have a circuit condition of low power factor in which a large current is flowing but which actually involves relatively little actual power. This condition would occur if a very large capacitance or a large inductance having a very low resistance were connected in a circuit.

Measurement of Electrical Quantities

The most common electrical measurements that are made are measurements of voltage, current, and resistance. Meters that contain a moving element and pointer together with a resistor or resistor network are the common indicating device for most measurements.

Voltmeters. A direct current voltmeter consists usually of a coil of very fine wire suspended but free to rotate in a permanent magnetic field. This is called a D'Arsonval movement. A typical meter contains this movement together with a series resistance of several thousand ohms in series with the coil to limit the flow of

Figure 11–94. A series resistance and millivoltmeter combination make up the basic parts of a voltmeter.

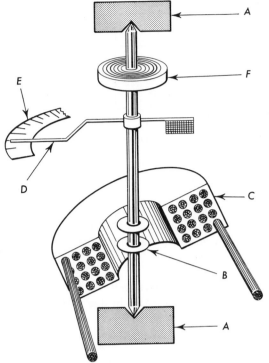

Figure 11–95. Iron vane type of alternating current meter. (A) Pivot bearings. (B) Soft iron discs on pivot shaft. (C) Cut away section of coil. (D) Pointer. (E) Scale. (F) Controlling spring. When current flows through the coil, a magnetic field is produced in the coil. The soft iron discs tend to align themselves along the lines of magnetism, and the pivot assembly will turn until the controlling spring torque balances the torque resulting from magnetic effects.

current to a few milliamperes. See Figure 11–94. A scale graduated in appropriate units completes the readout assembly. It is not usable on alternating current circuits without additional circuit components.

An alternating current voltmeter usually will be one of two kinds. An iron vane type of instrument consists of a stationary coil of wire carrying a current proportional to the impressed voltage to which it is connected. The magnetic field produced by current in the coil reacts with a pivoted iron vane to which a pointer is affixed. The scale over which the pointer moves is graduated in voltage units, Figure 11–95.

A second type of alternating current voltmeter is made with two coils, one fixed and one moving. When current goes through the coils, a magnetic field is produced in each coil that reacts with each other coil to produce a torque. This is called the electrodynamometer type of instrument.

A D'Arsonval type of movement can be used to measure voltage in AC circuits if a rectifier system is used to convert the ac to dc.

Ammeters. A D'Arsonval movement meter can be used to measure direct currents by permitting most of the current to flow through a very low resistance device called a "shunt," Figure 11–96. When current flows through the shunt, a voltage drop is produced that can be read on a millivoltmeter. Most shunts will have a voltage drop of either 50 millivolts (mv) or 100 mv when full rated current flows through them.

An ac ammeter can be made using the iron vane or electrodynamometer type of construction. In addition, for high frequency current measurements, a hot wire type or a rectifier type of meter is sometimes used. The hot wire type of current measuring instrument depends on the elongation of a straight wire due to the heat

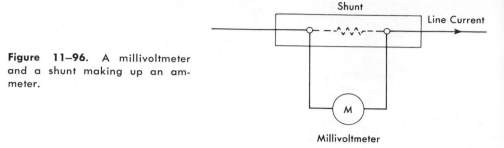

Figure 11–96. A millivoltmeter and a shunt making up an am- meter.

produced by current flowing through the wire. Its scale, like those of most ac meters, is nonlinear and is compressed at its low end.

Wattmeters. A common method of measuring electric power is to use a watt- meter. The usual form of wattmeter employs the dual coil construction of the electrodynamometer movement. With proper precautions, a wattmeter can be used to measure power either in dc or in ac circuits.

Bridge Measurements. A network of components arranged in a diamond shape is referred to as a bridge type of circuit. A typical resistive bridge is shown in Figure 11–97.

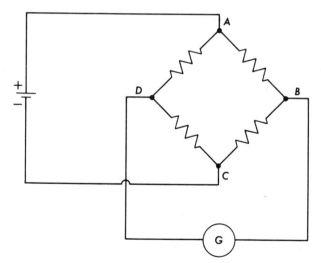

Figure 11–97. A typical re- sistive bridge circuit as used to indicate or measure resis- tance changes.

In this circuit, if the resistance path from *A* to *B* and *A* to *D* is the same resis- tance as the path from *B* to *C* and *D* to *C*, no current flow will be shown by the galvanometer "*G*." A galvanometer is a very sensitive D'Arsonval type of movement that will respond to currents in the microampere range.

However, if any one of the four resistances is changed in resistance a very small amount, a current will flow and will be indicated by the movement of the galvanometer pointer. If one of the other resistances is changed a known amount, it is possible to rebalance the bridge to give no current flow in the galvanometer. This type of circuit measurement is called a "null-method" of measurement, since it depends on balancing a known resistance against an unknown resistance to pro- duce a zero or null deflection of the indicating instrument.

It can be shown that the ratio of resistance at null balances is as follows:

$$\frac{R_{AB}}{R_{AD}} = \frac{R_{BC}}{R_{DC}}$$

If we know the ratio R_{AB} to R_{AD} and know the amount of resistance in ohms of R_{DC}, for example, then an unknown resistance R_{BC} can be computed.

Example: The ratio of R_{AB} to R_{AD} is 1 to 10. At bridge balance (null) conditions, the value of R_{DC} is 26.8 ohms. What is the value of R_{BC}?

SOLUTION:

$$R_{BC} = R_{DC}\left(\frac{R_{AB}}{R_{AD}}\right)$$
$$= 26.8\left(\frac{10}{1}\right)$$
$$= 268 \text{ ohms}$$

Note that the absolute values of R_{AB} and R_{AD} do not have to be known; only their ratio must be known.

Electron Tubes. Following the discovery by Edison that electrical charges could be transferred from a heated element in an evacuated space to another element in that space, DeForrest developed a device that could amplify electrical currents. The essential parts are shown in Figure 11–98.

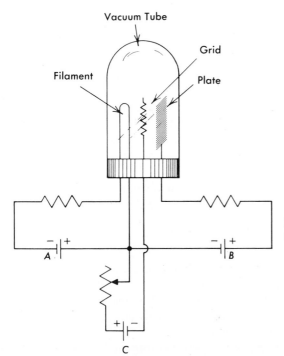

Figure 11–98. The essential parts of a three-element (triode) vacuum tube.

In this simplified diagram, a cell or battery at A heats a filament of tungsten that frequently is coated with material such as cesium or thorium. The heat "boils off" electrons from the filament surface and produces a cloud of negatively charged particles around the filament. If the plate is made electrically positive with respect to the filament by the battery "B," it is possible for the charges to flow through the evacuated space from the filament area to the plate and constitute a current flow. If the positive voltage of the plate is below a certain level or if the polarity is reversed to make the plate negative, no current will flow.

These two elements in an evacuated space constitute a diode and can be used to rectify alternating currents—that is, charge the ac to pulsating direct current.

If a third electrode is introduced between the filament and plate and is connected so it is negative with respect to the filament, the voltage of this third element, called a "grid," can block the current flow, even though the positively charged plate is attempting to attract electrons. In fact, because the grid is near the filament, a very small change in its voltage will make a large change in the filament-to-plate current flow. This constitutes the amplifying capability of the vacuum tube.

The Transistor

Shortly after the close of World War II, an announcement was made of the discovery of a solid state device, requiring no heated filament, that could be used as an amplifier. This discovery has, in only a few years, revolutionized the electronics industry. Although the solid state diode as a rectifier had been in use for many years, the introduction of another element to permit amplification provided a tremendous opportunity for miniaturizing electronic components. This new device was called a *transistor* and, as it made its appearance almost at the same time that the computer was being developed, it was incorporated into almost all modern computers.

The theory of the transistor is fairly complex, but its action depends essentially on the presence of minute quantities of an "impurity" material such as arsenic in a crystal of pure material such as germanium permitting current to flow in one direction but not in the other. A proper assembly of three sections of negative carrier and positive carrier material permits a small voltage to control a much larger current flow in a manner similar to the way a vacuum tube behaves in a circuit.

The major advantages of the transistor as used in electronic circuits are light weight, small space, low power consumption, and long life. The modern integrated circuit is made possible only by the use of semiconductor techniques, and permits a tiny chip of material to perform the same functions as a vacuum tube type of amplifier which would be thousands of times larger.

A fascinating new world of circuit design has been opened recently with the development of higher powered transistors, and now they can be used in all but the high current output stages of amplifiers.

Problems

11–123. Using a small compass, verify experimentally the pattern of magnetic lines around a bar magnet or a horseshoe magnet.

11–124. List, in order of increasing unit resistance, the ten best metallic conductors. In a word or two, give major advantages and disadvantages of using each as an electrical conductor for power circuits.

11–125. Sketch a simple circuit consisting of a crystal microphone, a vacuum tube or transistor used as an amplifier, and a loudspeaker. Explain briefly and concisely its features of operation in terms that might be used for a sales brochure.

11–126. A current of 5.5 ma flows from the filament to the plate of a vacuum tube. What is the approximate number of electrons flowing per second across the space?

11–127. A resistance of 3.65 kilohms is connected in series with 920 ohms. What is the combined resistance? If these two resistors are reconnected so they are in parallel, what will be the equivalent resistance?

11–128. Three resistors having values of 128 ohms, 144 ohms, and 98.2 ohms, respectively, are connected in series. What will be their combined resistance? If these three resistances are reconnected so they are in parallel with each other, what will their equivalent resistance be?

11–129. A current of 75.5 ma flows through a 1.80 kilohm resistance in a circuit containing a vacuum tube. What will be the voltage drop across the resistance? If the current is measured later and is found to have decreased to 48.1 ma, what things could have caused the decrease?

11–130. A circuit is suspected of having damaged insulation at some place in its installation on an aircraft. In order to check the insulation, a battery having a voltage of about 50 v is connected to the ship's metal structure and in series with the suspected circuit using a microammeter having an internal resistance of 100 ohms. If the microammeter reads 7.4 μa, what is the approximate resistance to ground of the circuit?

11–131. A battery having an internal resistance of 0.01 ohm and an open circuit voltage of 27.6 v is connected to a starter on an aircraft. If the starter resistance while not turning is 0.10 ohm and the line resistance of the connecting wires is 0.03 ohm, what maximum current can flow through the starter? What will be the voltage across the starter at the instant of closing the starting circuit?

11–132. Power in watts in a dc electric circuit is defined as the product of current in amperes and voltage in volts. If a 100 w lamp is connected to a 117 v line, what current will flow through the lamp? If a 40 w lamp is connected in parallel with the 100 w lamp, what total current will need to flow in the line supplying both lamps?

11–133. In the circuit of Figure 11–91, if the voltage of the cells is changed to an unknown amount but the current I_1 is measured to be 7.03 amp, what will be the values of V_1, V_2, V_3, V_4, I_2, I_3, I_4, and total cell voltages?

11–134. A dc voltage is to be measured which is known to be about 75 v. A voltmeter is not available, but a dc microammeter having a full scale of 100 μa and a resistance of 100 ohms is on hand. A large quantity of precision resistors is available. What series resistor should be chosen to make the meter show full scale deflection if 100 v is applied across it with a suitable resistor in series? (This will make the scale "direct reading.")

11–135. A dc shunt is to be made to permit the measurement of starting currents in an automotive starter. The expected current should not exceed 200 amp from a 12 v system. What should be the resistance of the shunt so that a current of 200 amp through it will produce a voltage drop of 50 mv across it?

Problems (continued)

11–136. A set of instructions accompanying an electrodynamic movement watt-meter says that a wattmeter should always have an ammeter and voltmeter in the circuit when the wattmeter is being used. Why is this desirable?

11–137. A Wheatstone bridge is set up with a ratio of 1:100 in the *AB* and *AD* sections of the bridge (see Figure 11–97). If the galvanometer shows no appreciable deflection when the resistance of *BC* is 157.1 ohms, what will be the resistance of *CD*? If there is a barely discernible deflection of the galvanometer when the resistance of *BC* is changed by ±0.3 ohms, what is the per cent uncertainty of the measurement of *CD*?

11–138. When using a Wheatstone bridge, what things might account for resistance measurements below 1 ohm being subject to considerable uncertainty?

11–139. If a change in plate voltage of 35.0 v in a vacuum tube produces a change in plate current of 2.20 ma and if a corresponding change of grid voltage of 1.7 voltage will produce the same change in plate current, what is the relative effectiveness of the change in plate voltage to change in grid voltage to produce the same change in each case of plate current? This ratio is known as amplification factor.

11–140. The life of an incandescent lamp varies approximately inversely as the 12th power of the applied voltage. If the rated life of a lamp is 800 hr at 117 v, what would be the expected life if operated continuously at 120 v? What would be the expected life if operated at 110 v?

11–141. If energy cost is 2 cents per kw hr, what will be the approximate cost of operating a 100 w lamp an average of 5 hr per day for a month?

11–142. Four strain gages having a resistance of 350.0 ohms each, are cemented to a steel bar to measure surface strain. When the bar is strained and the bridge is slightly unbalanced by the strain, a galvanometer having a resistance of 30.5 ohms indicates a current flow of 12.3 μa. What would be the voltage between points *B* and *D* (see Figure 11–97) of the Wheatstone bridge network?

11–143. A series circuit is made up using a 10,000 ohm resistance, a 3000 ohm resistance and an ammeter having a resistance of 720 ohms, all connected to a battery. If the ammeter shows a current flow of 3.03 ma, what voltage is supplied by the battery? What voltage drop would exist across the 3000 ohm resistance when this current is flowing?

11–144. A galvanometer used to measure small currents requires a connection to a circuit having an equivalent resistance of 350 ohms in order to help provide proper damping for reading oscillatory currents. If the strain gages making up a Wheatstone bridge to which the galvanometer is connected measure 120 ohms each, what resistance will need to be included in the circuit in order to provide proper matching resistance for the galvanometer?

11–145. A galvanometer used to measure small currents requires a connection to a circuit having an equivalent resistance of 120 ohms in order to help provide proper damping for reading oscillatory currents. If the strain gages making up a Wheatstone bridge to which the galvanometer is connected measure 350 ohms, what resistance will need to be included in the circuit in order to provide proper matching resistance for the galvanometer?

Appendix I

Logarithms – The Mathematical Basis for the Slide Rule

LAWS OF LOGARITHMS

Since a logarithm is an exponent, all the laws of exponents should be reviewed. Let us examine a few of these laws.

Exponential Law I: $(a)^m (a)^n = a^{m+n}$

We can put the equation above in statement form, since we know that logarithms are exponents and therefore follow the laws of exponents.

Law I. The logarithm of a product equals the sum of the logarithms of the factors.

Example:
$$(5)(7) = ?$$
$$\log_{10} 5 + \log_{10} 7 = \log_{10} \text{ans.}$$
$$0.6990 + 0.8451 = \log \text{ans.}$$
$$1.5441 = \log \text{ans.}$$
$$\text{Answer} = (3.50)(10)^1$$

This is true because
$$5 = (10)^{0.6990}$$
$$7 = (10)^{0.8451}$$
$$\text{product} = (10)^{0.6990}(10)^{0.8451}$$
$$\text{product} = (10)^{0.6990 + 0.8451}$$
$$\text{product} = (10)^{1.5441}$$
$$\text{product} = (3.50)(10)^1$$

Exponential Law II: $\dfrac{a^m}{a^n} = a^{m-n}$

Putting the equation above in statement form, we obtain the following law.

Law II.   The logarithm of a quotient equals the logarithm of the dividend minus the logarithm of the divisor.

Example:

$$\tfrac{5}{4} = ?$$
$$\log 5 - \log 4 = \log \text{ ans.}$$
$$0.6990 - 0.6021 = \log \text{ ans.}$$
$$0.0969 = \log \text{ ans.}$$
$$\text{Answer} = 1.25$$

Law III.   The logarithm of the x power of a number equals x times the logarithm of the number.

Example:

$$(5)^3 = ?$$
$$3(\log 5) = \log \text{ ans.}$$
$$3(0.6990) = \log \text{ ans.}$$
$$2.0970 = \log \text{ ans.}$$
$$\text{Answer} = (1.25)(10)^2$$

Law IV.   The logarithm of the x root of a number equals the logarithm of the number divided by x.

Example:

$$\sqrt[3]{3375} = ?$$

$$\frac{\log 3375}{3} = \log \text{ ans.}$$

$$\frac{3.5282}{3} = \log \text{ ans.}$$

$$1.1761 = \log \text{ ans.}$$
$$\text{Answer} = (1.50)(10)^1$$

NOTE: Law IV is actually a special case of Law III.
In some instances a combination of Law III and Law IV may be used.

Example:

$$(0.916)^{\frac{3}{4.15}} = ?$$

$$\frac{(\log 0.916)(3)}{4.15} = \log \text{ ans.}$$

$$\frac{(9.9619 - 10)(3)}{4.15} = \log \text{ ans.}$$

Perform multiplication first:

$$\frac{29.8857 - 30}{4.15} = \log \text{ ans.}$$

To be divided by 4.15, the negative number must be divisible a whole number of times. Therefore, the characteristic (which is $- 1$) is written as $414.0000 - 415$.

There are several values which could be chosen, such as $4149.0000 - 4150$, which would satisfy the condition that the characteristic be -1. Rewriting and dividing,

$$\frac{414.8857 - 415}{4.15} = \log \text{ ans.}$$

$$99.9725 - 100 = \log \text{ ans.}$$

$$\text{Answer} = (9.39)(10)^{-1}$$

The Cologarithm. Many times it is helpful to use the cologarithm of a number rather than the logarithm. The cologarithm of a number is the logarithm of the reciprocal of the number. The cologarithm is also the difference between the logarithm and the logarithm of unity.

Example:
$$\text{colog } 5 = \log \frac{1}{5}$$
$$= \log 1 - \log 5$$
$$= 0.0000 - 0.6990$$
$$= -0.6990$$

Since log 5 equals 0.6990, we see that the colog $x = -\log x$. Therefore:

1. The logarithm of the quotient of two numbers equals the logarithm of the dividend plus the cologarithm of the divisor.
2. The logarithm of the product of two numbers equals the logarithm of one number minus the cologarithm of the other number.

Natural Logarithms. When certain derivations of engineering formulas are made, a term may appear that contains a natural logarithm. For example, the magnetic field intensity near a current-carrying conductor varies with distance from the conductor according to a logarithmic pattern. In advanced texts it may be shown that a natural logarithm function, when plotted, gives an exponential curve whose slope at any point is equal to the ordinate at that point.

In solving problems involving natural logarithms, tables of natural logarithms can be used if they are available, or the natural logarithm, frequently abbreviated as "ln," may be converted to a logarithm to the base 10. To perform this latter operation, an algebraic transformation called *change of logarithmic base* is used. This transformation can be performed as follows:

$$\text{Natural logarithm} = (\text{common log})(\log_\epsilon 10)$$

Since $\log_\epsilon 10 = 2.3026$, we may write:

$$\text{Natural logarithm} = (\text{common log})(2.3026)$$

If natural logarithms are computed, it must be remembered that the mantissa is not independent of the location of the decimal point. Therefore, the same sequence of significant figures does not have the same mantissa, as is the case with common logarithms.

Example: Find the natural logarithm of 245

$$\log_{10} 245 = 2.3892$$
$$\ln 245 = (2.3892)(2.3026)$$
$$= 5.5014$$

Example: Find the natural logarithm of 2.45

$$\log_{10} 245 = 0.3892$$
$$\ln 2.45 = (0.3892)(2.3026)$$
$$= 0.8961$$

The natural logarithm of a number less than 1 is a negative number.

Example: Find the natural logarithm of 0.245

$$\log_{10} 0.245 = 9.3892 - 10$$

Since the logarithm has a negative characteristic, we can solve by first finding the colog and then multiplying by $\log_\epsilon 10$.

$$\text{colog}_{10} 0.245 = -0.6108$$
$$\ln 0.245 = (-0.6108)(2.3026)$$
$$= -1.4064$$

Appendix II

Trigonometry

RIGHT TRIANGLES

It can be shown by measurements and by formal derivations that for any given size of an angle at A or C, the ratio of the lengths of the sides to each other in a right triangle is a constant regardless of the numerical value of the lengths.

Figure A II–1.

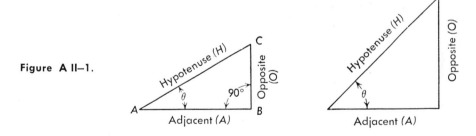

In Figure AII–1, the sides of a right triangle are named in reference to the angle under consideration. In these cases, the angle is designated as θ (theta).

Ratios of the sides are as follows:

$$\frac{\text{opposite side}}{\text{hypotenuse}} = \text{Sine } \theta \qquad \frac{O}{H} = \text{Sin } \theta \qquad \frac{\text{adjacent side}}{\text{opposite side}} = \text{Cotangent } \theta \quad \frac{A}{O} = \text{Cot } \theta$$

$$\frac{\text{adjacent side}}{\text{hypotenuse}} = \text{Cosine } \theta \qquad \frac{A}{H} = \text{Cos } \theta \qquad \frac{\text{hypotenuse}}{\text{adjacent side}} = \text{Secant } \theta \quad \frac{H}{A} = \text{Sec } \theta$$

$$\frac{\text{opposite side}}{\text{adjacent side}} = \text{Tangent } \theta \qquad \frac{O}{A} = \text{Tan } \theta \qquad \frac{\text{hypotenuse}}{\text{opposite side}} = \text{Cosecant } \theta \quad \frac{H}{O} = \text{Csc } \theta$$

141

METHODS OF SOLVING OBLIQUE TRIANGLE PROBLEMS

In order to solve an oblique triangle problem, at least three of the six parts of the triangle must be known, and at least one of the known parts must be a side. In the suggested methods listed below, only the most effective methods are given.

1. Given: two sides and an angle opposite one of them:
   a. Law of sines
   b. Right triangles
2. Given: two angles and one side:
   a. Law of sines
   b. Right triangles
3. Given: two sides and the included angle
   a. Law of cosines (answer is usually not dependable to more than three significant figures).
   b. Right triangles.
4. Given: three sides only:
   a. Tangent formula (half-angle solution)
   b. Sine formula (half-angle solution). This formula is not exact if the half-angle is near 90°.
   c. Cosine formula (half-angle solution). This formula is not exact if the half-angle is about 6° or less.
   d. Cosine formula (whole angle solution)
   e. Law of cosines (answer is usually not dependable to more than three significant figures).

METHODS FOR FINDING AREAS OF OBLIQUE TRIANGLES

The area of an oblique triangle may be found by any of several methods. Some of the more common methods are given below:

1. Area = (½) (base) (altitude).
2. Area = $\sqrt{(S)(S-AB)(S-BC)(S-AC)}$, where S = ½ perimeter of the triangle.
3. Area = ½ (product of two sides) (sine of the included angle).

SINE LAW

In any triangle the ratio of the length of a side to the sine of the angle opposite that side is the same as the ratio of any other side to the sine of the angle opposite it. In symbol form:

$$\frac{AB}{\sin \measuredangle C} = \frac{BC}{\sin \measuredangle A} = \frac{AC}{\sin \measuredangle B}$$

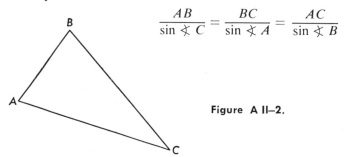

Figure A II–2.

This expression is called the *sine law*. The student is cautioned not to confuse the meanings of sine functions and sine law.

In the event one of the angles of a triangle is larger than 90°, a simple way to obtain the value of the sine of the angle is to subtract the angle from 180° and obtain the sine of this angle to use in the sine law expression.

The sine law can also be used if two sides and an angle of a triangle are known, provided the angle is not the one included between the sides. However, as explained in trigonometry texts, the product of the sine of the angle and the side adjacent must be equal to or less than the side opposite the angle; otherwise no solution is possible.

As an alternate method, the general triangle can be made into right triangles by adding construction lines. This method of using right triangle solutions is as exact as the sine law but usually will take more time than the sine law method.

COSINE LAW

In an oblique triangle, the square of any side is equal to the sum of the squares of the other two sides minus twice the product of the other two sides times the cosine of the included angle. In symbol form:

$$(AB)^2 = (AC)^2 + (BC)^2 - (2)(AC)(BC)(\cos \measuredangle C)$$

This expression is called the *cosine law* and is useful in many problems, although it may not give an answer to the desired precision since we are adding and subtracting terms that have only three significant figures.

After the side AB has been determined, the angles at A and B can be found by using the law of sines.

In the event that the angle used in the cosine law formula is larger than 90°, subtract the angle from 180°, and determine the cosine of this angle. Remember, however, that the cosine of an angle between 90° and 180° is negative. If the angle used in the formula is larger than 90°, the last term will add to the squared terms.

The problem above can also be solved by using construction lines and making right triangles from the figure. To do this, we construct the line BD perpendicular to AC. This will form two right triangles, ABD and BCD. In triangle BCD, side BD may be found by using BC and the sine of $\measuredangle C$. In a similar manner, by using the cosine of $\measuredangle C$, side DC may be found. From this we can determine side AD in triangle ABD.

Using the tangent function, the angle at A can be found, and AB can be determined by the use of the sine or cosine function or the Pythagorean theorem $(AB)^2 = (BD)^2 + (AD)^2$. The right triangle method, while it may take longer to solve, will in general give a more accurate answer.

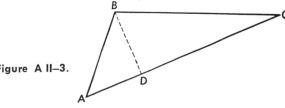

Figure A II–3.

THREE SIDES LAWS

There are a number of formulas derived in trigonometry that will give the angles of an oblique triangle when only three sides are known. The formulas differ considerably in ease of application and precision, especially if logarithms are used. Of

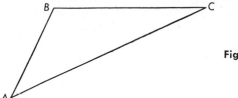

Figure A II–4.

all the formulas available, in general the half-angle (tangent) formula is better than others. The formula (half-angle solution) is as follows:

$$\tan \tfrac{1}{2} A = \frac{r}{S - BC}$$

where
$$r = \sqrt{\frac{(S - AB)(S - AC)(S - BC)}{S}}$$

and
$$S = \tfrac{1}{2} \text{ perimeter of triangle}$$

Other formulas that may be used are:

Sine formula (half-angle solution) $\sin \tfrac{1}{2} A = \sqrt{\dfrac{(S - AC)(S - AB)}{(AC)(AB)}}$

Cosine formula (half-angle solution) $\cos \tfrac{1}{2} A = \sqrt{\dfrac{(S)(S - BC)}{(AC)(AB)}}$

Cosine formula (whole angle solution) $\cos A = \dfrac{(2S)(S - BC)}{(AB)(AC)} - 1$

In the last formula, the quantity $(2S)(S - BC)/(AB)(AC)$ will usually be between 1 and 2 and can be read to four figures on the slide rule. Subtracting the 1 in the equation will leave the cosine of the angle correct to three figures. The formula has the advantage that it requires fewer operations. Also it is convenient to use if the slide rule is employed in solving problems.

After finding one angle, the remaining angles can be found by successive applications of the law, being careful to use the proper side of the triangle in the formula. The sine law can also be used after one angle is found. In order to have a check on the solution, it is better to solve for all three angles rather than solve for two angles, and then subtract their sum from 180°. If each angle is computed separately, their sum should be within the allowable error range of 180°.

As an incidental item in the tangent formula, the constant r is equal to the length of the radius of a circle that can be inscribed in the triangle.

Appendix III

Geometric Figures

Rectangle

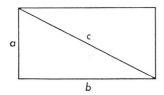

Area = (base)(altitude) = ab
Diagonal = $\sqrt{(\text{altitude})^2 + (\text{base})^2}$
$$C = \sqrt{a^2 + b^2}$$

Right Triangle

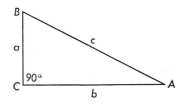

Angle A + angle B = angle C = $90°$
Area = ½ (base)(altitude)
Hypotenuse = $\sqrt{(\text{altitude})^2 + (\text{base})^2}$
$$C = \sqrt{a^2 + b^2}$$

Any Triangle

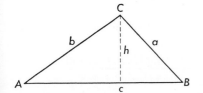

Angles $A + B + C = 180°$
(Altitude h is perpendicular to base c)
Area = ½ (base)(altitude)

145

Parallelogram

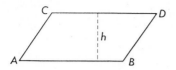

Area = (base)(altitude)
Altitude h is perpendicular to base AB
Angles $A + B + C + D = 360°$

Trapezoid

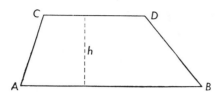

Area = ½ (altitude)(sum of bases)
(Altitude h is perpendicular to sides AB and CD. Side AB is parallel to side CD.)

Regular Polygon

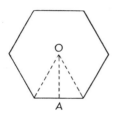

$$\text{Area} = \frac{1}{2} \begin{bmatrix} \text{length of} \\ \text{one side} \end{bmatrix} \begin{bmatrix} \text{Number} \\ \text{of sides} \end{bmatrix} \begin{bmatrix} \text{Distance} \\ OA \text{ to} \\ \text{center} \end{bmatrix}$$

A regular polygon has equal angles and equal sides and can be inscribed in or circumscribed about a circle.

Circle

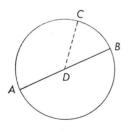

AB = diameter, CD = radius
Area = $\pi(\text{radius})^2 = \dfrac{\pi(\text{diameter})^2}{4}$
Circumference = $\pi(\text{diameter})$
$C = 2\pi(\text{radius})$
$\dfrac{\text{arc } BC}{\text{circumference}} = \dfrac{\text{angle } BDC}{360°}$
1 radian = $\dfrac{180°}{\pi} = 57.2958°$

Sector of a Circle

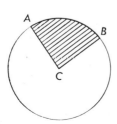

$$\text{Area} = \frac{(\text{arc } AB)(\text{radius})}{2}$$
$$= \pi \frac{(\text{radius})^2(\text{angle } ACB)}{360°}$$
$$= \frac{(\text{radius})^2 \ (\text{angle } ACB \text{ in radians})}{2}$$

Segment of a Circle

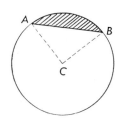

$$\text{Area} = \frac{(\text{radius})^2}{2}\left[\frac{\pi(\measuredangle ACB°)}{180} - \sin ACB°\right]$$

$$\text{Area} = \frac{(\text{radius})^2}{2}\left[\measuredangle ACB \text{ in radians} - \sin ACB°\right]$$

$$\text{Area} = \text{area of sector } ACB - \text{area of triangle } ABC$$

Ellipse

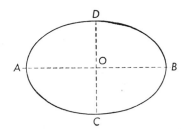

$$\text{Area} = \pi(\text{long radius } OA)(\text{short radius } OC)$$

$$\text{Area} = \frac{\pi}{4}(\text{long diameter } AB)(\text{short diameter } CD)$$

Volume and Center of Gravity Equations*

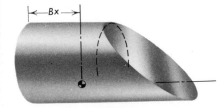

Volume equations are included for all cases. Where the equation for the CG (center of gravity) is not given, you can easily obtain it by looking up the volume and CG equations for portions of the shape and then combining values. For example, for the shape above, use the equations for a cylinder, Fig. 1, and a truncated cylinder, Fig. 10 (subscripts C and T, respectively, in the equations below). Hence taking moments

$$B_x = \frac{V_C B_C + V_T(B_T + L_C)}{V_C + V_T}$$

or $$B_x = \frac{\left(\frac{\pi}{4}D^2 L_C\right)\left(\frac{L_C}{2}\right) + \frac{\pi}{8}D^2 L_T\left(\frac{5}{16}L_T + L_C\right)}{\frac{\pi}{4}D^2 L_C + \frac{\pi}{8}D^2 L_T}$$

$$B_x = \frac{L^2_C + L_T\left(\frac{5}{16}L_T + L_C\right)}{2L_C + L_T}$$

In the equations to follow, angle θ can be either in degrees or in radians.

Thus θ (rad) $= \pi\theta/180$ (deg) $= 0.01745\,\theta$ (deg).

For example, if $\theta = 30$ deg in Case 3, then $\sin\theta = 0.5$ and

$$B = \frac{2R\,(0.5)}{3\,(30)\,(0.01745)} = 0.637R$$

Symbols used are:

B = distance from CG to reference plane,

V = volume,

D and d = diameter,

R and r = radius,

H = height,

L = length.

---

1. Cylinder

$$V = \frac{\pi}{4}D^2L = 0.7854D^2L \qquad \begin{matrix} B_1 = L/2 \\ B_2 = R \end{matrix}$$

Area of cylindrical surface
= (Perimeter of base) (perpendicular height)

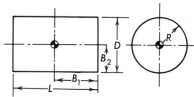

2. Half cylinder

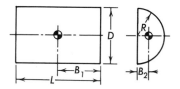

$$V = \frac{\pi}{8}D^2L = 0.3927D^2L$$

$$B_1 = L/2 \qquad B_2 = \frac{4R}{3\pi} = 0.4244R$$

3. Sector of cylinder

$$V = \theta\,R^2L \qquad B = \frac{2R\sin\theta}{3\theta}$$

4. Segment of cylinder

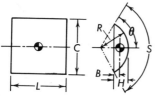

$$V = LR^2 \left(\theta - \frac{1}{2} \sin 2\theta\right)$$
$$V = 0.5L \left[RS - C (R - H)\right]$$

$$B = \frac{4R \sin^3 \theta}{6\theta - 3 \sin 2\theta}$$

$$S = 2R\theta$$
$$H = R (1 - \cos \theta)$$
$$C = 2R \sin \theta$$

5. Quadrant of cylinder

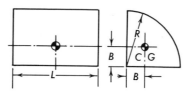

$$V = \frac{\pi}{4} R^2 L = 0.7854 R^2 L$$

$$B = \frac{4R}{3\pi} = 0.4244R$$

6. Fillet or spandrel

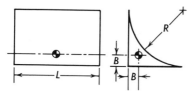

$$V = \left(1 - \frac{\pi}{4}\right) R^2 L = 0.2146 R^2 L$$

$$B = \frac{10 - 3\pi}{12 - 3\pi} R = 0.2234R$$

7. Hollow cylinder

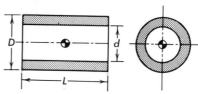

$$V = \frac{\pi L}{4} (D^2 - d^2)$$

CG at center of part

8. Half hollow cylinder

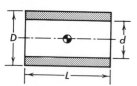

$$V = \frac{\pi L}{8} (D^2 - d^2)$$

$$B = \frac{4}{3\pi} \left[\frac{R^3 - r^3}{R^2 - r^2}\right]$$

9. Sector of hollow cylinder

 10. Truncated cylinder
(with full circle base)

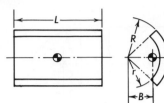

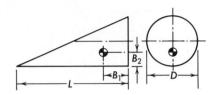

$V = 0.01745 \, (R^2 - r^2) \, \theta L$

$B = \dfrac{38.1972 \, (R^3 - r^3) \sin \theta}{(R^2 - r^2) \, \theta}$

$V = \dfrac{\pi}{8} D^2 L = 0.3927 D^2 L$

$B_1 = 0.3125L$

$B_2 = 0.375D$

---

 11. Truncated cylinder (with partial circle base)

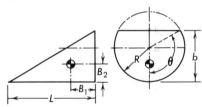

$b = R \, (1 - \cos \theta)$

$$V = \dfrac{R^3 L}{b} \left[\sin \theta - \dfrac{\sin^3 \theta}{3} - \theta \cos \theta \right]$$

$$B_1 = \dfrac{L \left[\dfrac{\theta \cos^2 \theta}{2} - \dfrac{5 \sin \theta \cos \theta}{8} + \dfrac{\sin^3 \theta \cos \theta}{12} + \dfrac{\theta}{8} \right]}{\left[1 - \cos \theta \right] \left[\sin \theta - \dfrac{\sin^3 \theta}{3} - \theta \cos \theta \right]}$$

$$B_2 = \dfrac{2R \left[-\dfrac{\theta \cos \theta}{2} + \dfrac{\sin \theta}{2} - \dfrac{\theta}{8} + \dfrac{\sin \theta \cos \theta}{8} - N \right]}{\left[\sin \theta - \dfrac{\sin^3 \theta}{3} - \theta \cos \theta \right]}$$

$$\text{where } N = \dfrac{\sin^3 \theta}{6} - \dfrac{\sin^3 \theta \cos \theta}{12}$$

12. Oblique cylinder
(or circular hole at oblique angle)

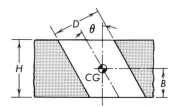

$$V = \frac{\pi}{4} D^2 \frac{H}{\cos \theta} = 0.7854 D^2 H \sec \theta$$

$$B = H/2 \qquad r = \frac{d}{2}$$

13. Bend in cylinder

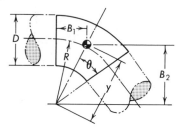

$$V = \frac{\pi^2}{360} D^2 R \theta = 0.0274 D^2 R \theta$$

$$y = R \left[1 + \frac{r^2}{4R^2} \right] \qquad \begin{array}{l} B_1 = y \tan \theta \\ B_2 = y \cot \theta \end{array}$$

14. Curved groove in cylinder

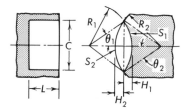

$$\sin \theta_1 = \frac{C}{2R_1} \qquad \sin \theta_2 = \frac{C}{2R_2} \qquad S = 2R\theta$$

$$H_1 = R_1 (1 - \cos \theta_1) \qquad H_2 = R_2 (1 - \cos \theta_2)$$

$$V = L \left[R_1^2 \left(\theta_1 - \frac{1}{2} \theta_1 \sin 2\theta_1 \right) + R_2^2 \left(\theta_2 - \frac{1}{2} \theta_2 \sin 2\theta_2 \right) \right]$$

Compute *CG* of each part separately

15. Slot in cylinder

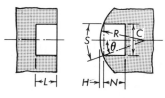

$$H = R (1 - \cos \theta) \qquad \sin \theta = \frac{C}{2R}$$

$$S = 2R\theta$$

$$V = L \left[CN + R^2 \left(\theta - \frac{1}{2} \sin 2\theta \right) \right]$$

16. Slot in hollow cylinder

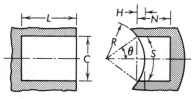

$$S = 2R\theta \qquad \sin \theta = \frac{C}{2R}$$

$$H = R (1 - \cos \theta)$$

$$V = L \left[CN - R^2 \left(\theta - \frac{1}{2} \sin 2\theta \right) \right]$$

$$V = L \left\{ CN - 0.5 \left[RS - C (R - H) \right] \right\}$$

17. Curved groove in hollow cylinder

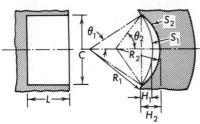

$$\sin \theta_1 = \frac{C}{2R_1} \qquad \sin \theta_2 = \frac{C}{2R_2} \qquad S = 2R\theta$$

$$H_1 = R_1 (1 - \cos \theta_1)$$

$$H_2 = R_2 (1 - \cos \theta_2)$$

$$V = L\left(\left[R_2^2 \left(\theta_2 - \frac{1}{2}\sin 2\theta_2\right)\right] - \left[R_1^2 \left(\theta_1 - \frac{1}{2}\sin 2\theta_1\right)\right]\right)$$

$$V = \frac{L}{2}\left(\left[R_2 S_2 - C (R_2 - H_2)\right] - \left[R_1 S_1 - C (R_1 - H_1)\right]\right)$$

18. Slot through hollow cylinder

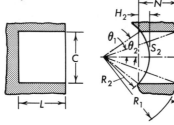

$$\sin \theta_1 = \frac{C}{R_1} \qquad \sin \theta_2 = \frac{C}{R_2}$$

$$S = 2R\theta$$

$$H_1 = R_1 (1 - \cos \theta_1)$$

$$H_2 = R_2 (1 - \cos \theta_2)$$

$$V = L\left(CN + \left[R_1^2 \left(\theta_1 - \frac{1}{2}\sin 2\theta_1\right)\right] - \left[R_2 \left(\theta_2 - \frac{1}{2}\sin 2\theta_2\right)\right]\right)$$

$$V = L\left(CN + 0.5\,[R_1 S_1 - C (R_1 - H_1)] - 0.5\,[R_2 S_2 - C (R_2 - H_2)]\right)$$

19. Intersecting cylinder (volume of junction box)

$$V = D^3 \left(\frac{\pi}{2} - \frac{2}{3}\right) = 0.9041 D^3$$

20. Intersecting hollow cylinders (volume of junction box)

$$V = \left(\frac{\pi}{2} - \frac{2}{3}\right)(D^3 - d^3) - \frac{\pi}{2} d^2 (D - d)$$

$$V = 0.9041 (D^3 - d^3) - 1.5708 d^2 (D - d)$$

21. Intersecting parallel cylinders
$(M < R_1)$

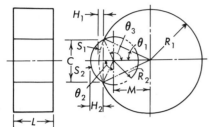

$$\theta_2 = 180° - \theta_3 \qquad \cos \theta_3 = \frac{R_2^2 + M^2 - R_1^2}{2MR_2}$$

$$\cos \theta_1 = \frac{R_1^2 + M^2 - R_2^2}{2MR_1}$$

$$H_1 = R_1 (1 - \cos \theta_1)$$
$$S_1 = 2R_1\theta_1$$

$$V = L \left(\pi R_1^2 + \left[R_2^2 \left(\theta_2 - \frac{1}{2} \sin 2\theta_2\right) \right] - \left[R_1^2 \left(\theta_1 - \frac{1}{2} \sin 2\theta_1\right) \right] \right)$$

22. Intersecting parallel cylinders $(M > R_1)$

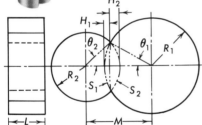

$$H_1 = R_1 (1 - \cos \theta_1)$$
$$S_1 = 2R_1\theta_1$$

$$\cos \theta_1 = \frac{R_1^2 + M^2 - R_2^2}{2MR_1}$$

$$V = L \left(\left[\pi (R_1^2 + R_2^2) \right] - \left[R_1^2 \left(\theta_1 - \frac{1}{2} \sin 2\theta_1\right) \right] - \left[R_2^2 \left(\theta_2 - \frac{1}{2} \sin 2\theta_2\right) \right] \right)$$

23. Sphere

$$V = \frac{\pi D^3}{6} = 0.5236D^3$$

Area of surface $= 4\pi(\text{radius})^2 = \pi D^2$

24. Hemisphere

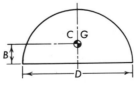

$$V = \frac{\pi D^3}{12} = 0.2618D^3$$

$$B = 0.375R$$

25. Spherical segment

 26. Spherical sector

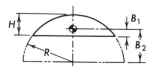

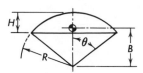

$$V = \pi H^2 \left(R - \frac{H}{3} \right)$$

$$B_1 = \frac{H\,(4R - H)}{4\,(3R - H)}$$

$$B_2 = \frac{3\,(2R - H)^2}{4\,(3R - H)}$$

$$V = \frac{2\pi}{3}\,R^2 H = 2.0944 R^2 H$$

$$B = 0.375\,(1 + \cos\theta)$$

$$R = 0.375\,(2R - H)$$

27. Shell of hollow hemisphere

28. Hollow sphere

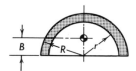

$$V = \frac{2\pi}{3}\,(R^3 - r^3)$$

$$B = 0.375 \left(\frac{R^4 - r^4}{R^3 - r^3} \right)$$

$$V = \frac{4\pi}{3}\,(R^3 - r^3)$$

29. Shell of spherical sector

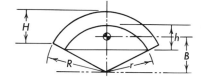

$$V = \frac{2\pi}{3}\,(R^2 H - r^2 h)$$

$$B = 0.375 \left\{ \frac{[R^2 H\,(2R - H)] - [r^2 h\,(2r - h)]}{R^2 H - r^2 h} \right\}$$

30. Shell of spherical segment

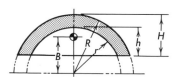

$$V = \pi \left[H^2 \left(R - \frac{H}{3} \right) - h^2 \left(r - \frac{h}{3} \right) \right]$$

$$B = \frac{3}{4} \frac{\left[\left(R - \frac{H}{3} \right) \dfrac{H^2\,(2R - H)^2}{3R - H} - \left(r - \frac{h}{3} \right) \dfrac{h^2\,(2r - h)^2}{3r - h} \right]}{H^2 \left(R - \frac{H}{3} \right) - h^2 \left(r - \frac{h}{3} \right)}$$

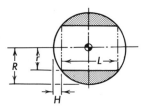

31. Circular hole through sphere

$$V = \pi \left[r^2 L + 2H^2 \left(R - \frac{H}{3} \right) \right]$$

$$H = R - \sqrt{R^2 - r^2}$$
$$L = 2(R - H)$$

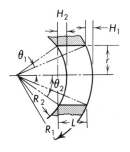

32. Circular hole through hollow sphere

$$V = \pi \left\{ r^2 L + H_1 \left(R_1 - \frac{H_1}{3} \right) - H_2^2 \left(R_2 - \frac{H_2}{3} \right) \right\}$$

$$\sin \theta_1 = r/R_1 \qquad \sin \theta_2 = r/R_2 \qquad H = R (1 - \cos \theta)$$

---

33. Spherical zone

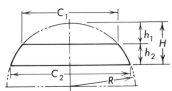

$$V = \pi \left\{ \left[H^2 \left(R - \frac{H}{3} \right) \right] - \left[h_1^2 \left(R - \frac{h_1}{3} \right) \right] \right\}$$

$$V = \frac{\pi h_2}{6} \left[\frac{3}{4} C_1^2 + \frac{3}{4} C_2^2 + h_2^2 \right]$$

34. Conical hole through spherical shell

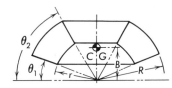

$$V = \frac{2\pi}{3} (R^3 - r^3) (\sin \theta_2 - \sin \theta_1)$$

$$B = \frac{0.375 (R^4 - r^4) (\sin \theta_2 + \sin \theta_1)}{R^3 - r^3}$$

---

35. Torus

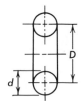

$$V = \frac{1}{4} \pi^2 d^2 D = 2.467 d^2 D$$

36. Hollow torus

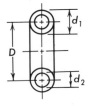

$$V = \frac{1}{4} \pi^2 D (d_1^2 - d_2^2)$$

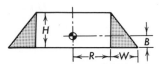 37. Bevel ring

 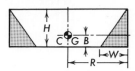 38. Bevel ring

$$V = \pi(R + \tfrac{1}{3}W)\,WH$$

$$B = H\left[\frac{\dfrac{R}{3}+\dfrac{W}{12}}{R+\dfrac{W}{3}}\right]$$

$$B > \frac{H}{3}$$

$$V = \pi\left(R - \tfrac{1}{3}W\right)WH$$

$$B = H\left[\frac{\dfrac{R}{3}-\dfrac{W}{12}}{R-\dfrac{W}{3}}\right]$$

 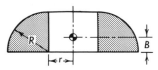 39. Quarter torus

$$B < 0.4244R$$

$$V = \frac{\pi^2 R^2}{2}\left(r + \frac{4R}{3\pi}\right) = 4.9348R^2\,(r + 0.4244R)$$

$$B = \frac{4R}{3\pi}\left[\frac{r + \dfrac{3R}{8}}{r + \dfrac{4R}{3\pi}}\right] = \frac{0.4244Rr + 0.1592R^2}{r + 0.4244R}$$

 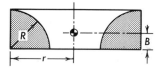 40. Quarter torus

 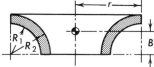 41. Curved shell ring

$$V = \frac{\pi^2 R^2}{2}\left[r - \frac{4R}{3\pi}\right]$$

$$B = \frac{4R}{3\pi}\left[\frac{r - \dfrac{3R}{8}}{r - \dfrac{4R}{3\pi}}\right]$$

$$V = 2\pi\left\{r - \frac{4}{3\pi}\left[\frac{R_2^3 - R_1^3}{R_2^2 - R_1^2}\right]\right\}\frac{\pi}{4}\,(R_2^2 - R_1^2)$$

$$B = \frac{4}{3\pi}\left[\frac{R_2^3\left(r - \dfrac{3}{8}R_2\right) - R_1^3\left(r - \dfrac{3}{8}R_1\right)}{(R_2^2 - R_1^2)\left\{r - \dfrac{4}{3\pi}\left[\dfrac{R_2^3 - R_1^3}{R_2^2 - R_1^2}\right]\right\}}\right]$$

42. Curved shell ring

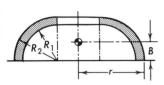

$$V = \frac{\pi^2}{2}\left[r(R_2^2 - R_1^2) + \frac{4}{3\pi}(R_2^3 - R_1^3)\right]$$

$$B = \frac{2}{\pi}\left[\frac{\frac{2r}{3}(R_2^3 - R_1^3) + \frac{1}{4}(R_2^4 - R_1^4)}{r(R_2^2 - R_1^2) + \frac{4}{3\pi}(R_2^3 - R_1^3)}\right]$$

43. Fillet ring

44. Fillet ring

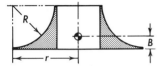

$$V = 2\pi R^2\left[\left(1 - \frac{\pi}{4}\right)r - \frac{R}{6}\right]$$

$$B = R\frac{\left[\left(\frac{5}{6} - \frac{\pi}{4}\right)r - \frac{R}{24}\right]}{\left(1 - \frac{\pi}{4}\right)r - \frac{R}{6}}$$

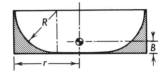

$$V = 2\pi R^2\left[\left(1 - \frac{\pi}{4}\right)r - \left(\frac{5}{6} - \frac{\pi}{4}\right)R\right]$$

$$B = R\frac{\left[\left(\frac{5}{6} - \frac{\pi}{4}\right)r - \left(\frac{19}{24} - \frac{\pi}{4}\right)R\right]}{\left(1 - \frac{\pi}{4}\right)r - \left(\frac{5}{6} - \frac{\pi}{4}\right)R}$$

45. Curved-sector ring

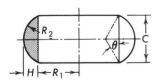

$$V = 2\pi R_2^2\left[R_1 + \left(\frac{4\sin 3\theta}{6\theta - 3\sin 2\theta} - \cos\theta\right)R_2\right]\left[\theta - 0.5\sin 2\theta\right]$$

46. Ellipsoidal cylinder

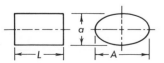

$$V = \frac{\pi}{4}AaL$$

47. Ellipsoid

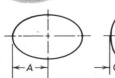

$$V = \frac{4}{3}\pi ACE$$

48. Paraboloid

49. Pyramid (with base of any shape)

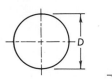

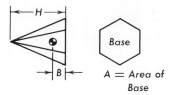

$$V = \frac{\pi}{8} HD^2 \qquad B = \frac{1}{3} H$$

A = Area of Base $\qquad V = \frac{1}{3} AH \qquad B = \frac{1}{4} H$

---

50. Frustum of pyramid
(with base of any shape)

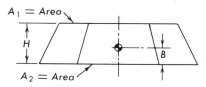

$$V = \frac{1}{3} H \left(A_1 + \sqrt{A_1 A_2} + A_2\right)$$

$$B = \frac{H \left(A_1 + 2\sqrt{A_1 A_2} + 3A_2\right)}{4 \left(A_1 + \sqrt{A_1 A_2} + A_2\right)}$$

51. Cone

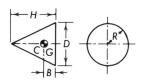

$$V = \frac{\pi}{12} D^2 H \qquad B = \frac{1}{4} H$$

Area of conical surface (right
cone) = ½ (circumference of base)
× (slant height)

---

52. Frustum of cone

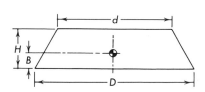

$$V = \frac{\pi}{12} H \left(D^2 + Dd + d^2\right)$$

$$B = \frac{H \left(D^2 + 2Dd + 3d^2\right)}{4 \left(D^2 + Dd + d^2\right)}$$

53. Frustum of hollow cone

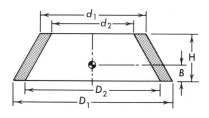

$$V = 0.2618H \left[\left(D_1^2 + D_1 d_1 + d_1^2\right) - \left(D_2^2 + D_2 d_2 + d_2^2\right)\right]$$

54. Hexagon

$$V = \frac{\sqrt{3}}{2} d^2 L$$
$$V = 0.866 d^2 L$$

55. Closely packed helical springs

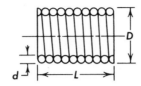

$$V = \frac{\pi^2 dL}{4} (D - d)$$
$$V = 2.4674 \, (D - d)$$

56. Rectangular prism

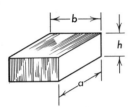

Volume = length × width × height
Volume = area of base × altitude

57. Any prism

(Axis either perpendicular or inclined to base)

Volume = (area of base)(perpendicular height)

Volume = (lateral length)(area of perpendicular cross-section)

Appendix IV

Tables

WEIGHTS AND MEASURES

Avoirdupois Weight

1 grain (avdp)	1 grain	1 grain (troy)
27 11/32 grain	1 dram	
16 dram	1 ounce (oz)	
16 ounces	1 pound (lb)	
100 pounds	1 hundredweight (cwt)	
2000 pounds	1 short ton (T)	
2240 pounds	1 long ton	

Metric Weight

10 milligram (mg)	1 centigram (cg)
10 centigram	1 decigram (dg)
10 decigram	1 gram (g)
10 gram	1 dekagram (Dg)
10 dekagram	1 hectogram (hg)
10 hectogram	1 kilogram (kg)

Mass and Force Equivalents

1 gram	0.03527 ounce	980.6 dynes	
1 kilogram	2.2046 pound	$(6.852)(10^{-2})$ slug	9.807 newton
1 metric ton	2205 pound		
1 pound	453.6 gram	0.4536 kilogram	4.448 newton
1 ounce	28.35 gram		
1 newton	10^5 dynes	0.2248 pounds	

Dry Measure

2 pints	1 quart (qt)	67.2 cubic inches (in.³)
8 quarts	1 peck	
4 pecks	1 bushel (bu)	

Liquid Measure

4 gill	1 pint (pt) 16 fluid ounces 2 cups
2 pints	1 quart
4 quarts	1 gallon (gal) 231 cubic inches
7.48 gallons	1 cubic foot (ft³)
31½ gallons	1 barrel (bbl)
1 British Imperial gallon	1.200 U.S. gallons

Linear Measure

1 mil	0.001 inch (in.)	
12 inches	1 foot (ft)	
3 feet	1 yard (yd)	
5½ yards	1 rod	
40 rods	1 furlong	
320 rods	1 mile 5280 ft 1760 yards	
3 miles	1 league	

Linear Measure Equivalents

6.08 feet	1 fathom
6080.2 feet	1 nautical mile
1 nautical mile	1.15 statute mile

1 knot is a speed of 1 nautical mile per hour

Metric Linear Measure

10 millimeter (mm)	1 centimeter (cm)
10 centimeter	1 decimeter (dm)
10 decimeter	1 meter (m)
10 meter	1 dekameter (Dm)
10 dekameter	1 hectometer (hm)
10 hectometer	1 kilometer (km)

Metric Linear Equivalents

1 centimeter	0.3937 inch 10^{-5} kilometer
1 meter	39.37 inches 1.0936 yard 3.281 feet
1 kilometer	0.62137 mile (approximately ⅝ mile) 3281 feet
1 inch	2.540 centimeter
1 foot	30.48 centimeter 0.3048 meter
1 mile	1.6093 kilometer
1 Angstrom	10^{-10} meter
1 micron (μ)	10^{-6} meter

Area Measure

144 square inches (in.²)	1 square foot (ft²)
9 square feet	1 square yard (yd²)
30¼ square yards	1 square rod
160 square rods	1 acre 4840 square yards 43,560 square feet
640 acres	1 square mile 1 section
2.47 acres	1 hectare (metric)
0.7854 square mils	1 circular mil $7.854(10^{-7})$ square inches

Volume Measure

1728 cubic inches	1 cubic foot (ft³)
27 cubic feet	1 cubic yard (yd³)
231 cubic inches	1 standard gallon (U.S.)
2150.42 cubic inches	1 standard bushel
144 cubic inches	1 board foot
61.02 cubic inches	1 liter (metric)

Conversion Equivalents

1 atmosphere	14.69 pounds per square inch (psi)
	29.92 inches of mercury
	406.8 inches of water
1 British thermal unit	252 calories (gram, at 15°C)
1 British thermal unit	778 foot-pounds (ft-lb) 0.00039 horsepower-hour
1 calorie	0.003968 British thermal unit
1 cubic inch	16.39 cubic centimeters 0.01639 liters
1 foot-pound per second	0.001818 horsepower (hp)
1 horsepower	746 watts 33,000 foot-pounds per minute
	550 foot-pounds per second
1 kilowatt	1.34 horsepower

Hydrostatic water pressure in pounds per square inch = (height in feet) (0.4332)

1 inch Hg (mercury)	0.491 pound per square inch
1 Joule	1 watt second 0.737 foot-pound 10^7 ergs
	$9.48(10^{-4})$ Btu
1 kilowatt-hour	3413 British thermal unit
	1.341 hp-hr
	$3.6(10^6)$ Joule
1 radian	57.2958 degrees
1 million electron volts (Mev)	$1.602(10^{-13})$ joule

COEFFICIENTS OF FRICTION

Average Values

SURFACES	STATIC	KINETIC
Metals on wood	0.4 —0.63	0.35—0.60
Wood on wood	0.3 —0.5	0.25—0.4
Leather on wood	0.38—0.45	0.3 —0.35
Iron on iron (wrought)	0.4 —0.5	0.4 —0.5
Glass on glass	0.23—0.25	0.20—0.25
Leather on glass	0.35—0.38	0.33—0.35
Wood on glass	0.35—0.40	0.28—0.31
Wood on sheet iron	0.43—0.50	0.38—0.45
Leather on sheet iron	0.45—0.50	0.35—0.40
Brass on wrought iron	0.35—0.45	0.30—0.35
Babbitt on steel	0.35—0.40	0.30—0.35
Steel on ice	0.03—0.04	0.03—0.04

THE GREEK ALPHABET

A	α	Alpha	N	ν	Nu
B	β	Bēta	Ξ	ξ	Xī
Γ	γ	Gamma	O	o	Omicron
Δ	δ	Delta	Π	π	Pī
E	ϵ	Epsilon	P	ρ	Rhō
Z	ζ	Zēta	Σ	$\sigma\varsigma$	Sigma
H	η	Eta	T	τ	Tau
Θ	θ	Thēta	Υ	υ	Upsilon
I	ι	Iōta	Φ	ϕ	Phī
K	κ	Kappa	X	χ	Chī
Λ	λ	Lambda	Ψ	ψ	Psī
M	μ	Mu	Ω	ω	Omega

DIMENSIONAL PREFIXES

SYMBOL	PREFIX	MULTIPLE
T	tera units	10^{12}
G	giga units	10^{9}
M	mega units	10^{6}
k	kilo units	10^{3}
h	hecto units	10^{2}
da	deca units	10^{1}
	units	10^{0}
d	deci units	10^{-1}
c	centi units	10^{-2}
m	milli units	10^{-3}
μ	micro units	10^{-6}
n	nano units	10^{-9}
p	pico units	10^{-12}
f	femto units	10^{-15}
a	atto units	10^{-18}

SPECIFIC GRAVITIES AND SPECIFIC WEIGHTS (Average Values)

MATERIAL	SPECIFIC GRAVITY	AVERAGE SPECIFIC WEIGHT IN LB$_f$/FT^3	MATERIAL	SPECIFIC GRAVITY	AVERAGE SPECIFIC WEIGHT IN LB$_f$/FT^3
Alcohol, ethyl	0.792	49.6	Limestone,		
Aluminum, cast	2.65	166	crushed	1.4—1.6	95
Air, S.T.P.	0.001293	0.0806	Marble	2.5—2.8	166
Babbitt metal,			Mercury	13.56	845
soft	9.75—10.65	625	Nickel	8.90	558
Brass, cast, red	8.4—8.7	530	Oil, lubricating	0.91	57
Brick, common	1.8—2.0	119	Paraffin	0.90	56
Cement, port-			Petroleum, crude	0.88	55
land, bags	1.44	90	Rubber	1.25	78
Chalk	2.25	140	Sand, loose, wet	1.9	120
Clay, loose, wet	1.7—1.8	110	Sandstone, solid	2.3	144
Coal, anthracite,			Sea water	1.03	64
solid	1.4—1.8	95	Silver	10.5	655
Coal, bitumi-			Steel, structural	7.9	490
nous, solid	1.2—1.5	85	Sulfur	1.9—2.1	125
Concrete, gravel,			Tin	7.3	456
sand	2.2—2.4	142	Turpentine	0.865	54
Copper, wire	8.93	560	Water, 4°C		
Cork	0.18—0.25	12.5	(39.2°F)	1.000	62.43
Earth	1.45—2.2	90—130	Water, 100°C		
Gasoline	0.68—0.72	44	(212°F)	0.96	59.83
Glass, crown	2.5—2.7	161	Wood seasoned:		
Glass, flint	3.0—3.6	205	Cedar	0.35—0.65	31
Glycerine	1.25	78	Cypress	0.48—0.57	32
Gold	19.3	1205	Ebony	1.2—1.3	78
Granite, solid	2.5—3.0	172	Fir	0.51—0.60	35
Gravel, loose, wet	1.45—1.90	105	Hickory	0.70—0.93	51
Ice	0.911	57	Mahogany	0.56—0.85	44
Iron, gray cast	7.00—7.12	450	Maple	0.68—0.80	45
Iron, wrought	7.6—7.9	480	Oak	0.70—0.90	50
Kerosene	0.8	50	Pine, white	0.38—0.48	28
Lead	11.34	710	Pine, yellow	0.65—0.75	44
Limestone, solid	2.5—2.9	168	Walnut	0.60—0.70	41
			Zinc	7.14	445

NOTE: The value for the specific weight of water, which is usually used in problem solutions, is 62.4 lb$_f$/ft^3 or 8.34 lb$_f$ per gallon.

TRIGONOMETRIC FUNCTIONS

$\sin(-\alpha) = -\sin\alpha$

$\cos(-\alpha) = \cos\alpha$

$\tan(-\alpha) = -\tan\alpha$

$\sin^2\alpha = \tfrac{1}{2} - \tfrac{1}{2}\cos 2\alpha$

$\cos^2\alpha = \tfrac{1}{2} + \tfrac{1}{2}\cos 2\alpha$

$\sin^2\alpha + \cos^2\alpha = 1$

$\sec^2\alpha = 1 + \tan^2\alpha$

$\csc^2\alpha = 1 + \text{ctn}^2\alpha$

$\sin 2\alpha = 2\sin\alpha\cos\alpha$

$\cos 2\alpha = \cos^2\alpha - \sin^2\alpha = 1 - 2\sin^2\alpha = 2\cos^2\alpha - 1$

$$\sin\alpha = \alpha - \frac{\alpha^3}{3!} + \frac{\alpha^5}{5!} - \frac{\alpha^7}{7!} + \frac{\alpha^9}{9!}\cdots$$

$$\cos\alpha = 1 - \frac{\alpha^2}{2!} + \frac{\alpha^4}{4!} - \frac{\alpha^6}{6!} + \frac{\alpha^8}{8!}\cdots$$

$\sin(\alpha \pm \theta) = \sin\alpha\cos\theta \pm \cos\alpha\sin\theta$

$\cos(\alpha \pm \theta) = \cos\alpha\cos\theta \mp \sin\alpha\sin\theta$

DIFFERENTIALS AND INTEGRALS

$$\frac{dx^n}{dx} = nx^{n-1}$$

$$\frac{d(uv)}{dx} = U\frac{dv}{dx} + V\frac{du}{dx}$$

$$\frac{d(u/v)}{dx} = \frac{V(du/dx) - U(dv/dx)}{v^2}$$

$$\int x^n dx = \frac{x^{n+1}}{n+1} + C$$

$$\int u\,dv = uv - \int v\,du$$

$$\int \frac{dx}{x} = \log_\epsilon x + C$$

$$\int \sin x\,dx = -\cos x + C$$

$$\int \cos x\,dx = \sin x + C$$

$$\int \sin^2 x\,dx = \frac{x}{2} - \frac{\sin 2x}{4} + C$$

$$\int \cos^2 x\,dx = \frac{x}{2} + \frac{\sin 2x}{4} + C$$

SPECIAL PURPOSE FORMULAS USEFUL IN SOLVING UNIFORM MOTION PROBLEMS

Legend

V—velocity $\qquad V_2$—final velocity $\qquad S$—distance $\qquad a$—acceleration

V_1—initial velocity $\quad V_{av}$—average velocity $\quad t$—time

GIVEN	TO FIND	SUGGESTED FORMULAS
$V_1,\ V_2,\ t$	S	$S = \left(\dfrac{V_1 + V_2}{2} \right) t$
$V_1,\ V_2,\ a$	S	$S = \dfrac{V_2^2 - V_1^2}{2a}$
$V_1,\ a,\ t$	S	$S = V_1 t + \dfrac{at^2}{2}$
$V_1,\ V_2$	V_{av}	$V_{av} = \dfrac{V_1 + V_2}{2}$
$S,\ t$	V_{av}	$V_{av} = \dfrac{S}{t}$
$V_2,\ a,\ t$	V_1	$V_1 = V_2 - at$
$V_2,\ a,\ S$	V_1	$V_1 = \sqrt{V_2^2 - 2aS}$
$S,\ a,\ t$	V_1	$V_1 = \dfrac{S}{t} - \dfrac{at}{2}$
$V_1,\ a,\ t$	V_2	$V_2 = V_1 + at$
$V_1,\ a,\ S$	V_2	$V_2 = \sqrt{V_1^2 + 2aS}$
$V_1,\ S,\ t$	V_2	$V_2 = \dfrac{2S}{t} - V_1$
$V_1,\ V_2,\ S$	t	$t = \dfrac{2S}{V_1 + V_2}$
$V_1,\ a,\ S$	t	$t = \dfrac{-V_1 \pm \sqrt{V_1^2 + 2aS}}{a}$
$V_1,\ V_2,\ a$	t	$t = \dfrac{V_2 - V_1}{a}$
$V_1,\ V_2,\ t$	a	$a = \dfrac{V_2 - V_1}{t}$
$V_1,\ V_2,\ S$	a	$a = \dfrac{V_2^2 - V_1^2}{2S}$
$V_1,\ S,\ t$	a	$a = \dfrac{2S}{t^2} - \dfrac{2V_1}{t}$

LOGARITHMS

Natural Numbers	0	1	2	3	4	5	6	7	8	9	PROPORTIONAL PARTS								
											1	2	3	4	5	6	7	8	9
10	0000	0043	0086	0128	0170	0212	0253	0294	0334	0374	4	8	12	17	21	25	29	33	37
11	0414	0453	0492	0531	0569	0607	0645	0682	0719	0755	4	8	11	15	19	23	26	30	34
12	0792	0828	0864	0899	0934	0969	1004	1038	1072	1106	3	7	10	14	17	21	24	28	31
13	1139	1173	1206	1239	1271	1303	1335	1367	1399	1430	3	6	10	13	16	19	23	26	29
14	1461	1492	1523	1553	1584	1614	1644	1673	1703	1732	3	6	9	12	15	18	21	24	27
15	1761	1790	1818	1847	1875	1903	1931	1959	1987	2014	3	6	8	11	14	17	20	22	25
16	2041	2068	2095	2122	2148	2175	2201	2227	2253	2279	3	5	8	11	13	16	18	21	24
17	2304	2330	2355	2380	2405	2430	2455	2480	2504	2529	2	5	7	10	12	15	17	20	22
18	2553	2577	2601	2625	2648	2672	2695	2718	2742	2765	2	5	7	9	12	14	16	19	21
19	2788	2810	2833	2856	2878	2900	2923	2945	2967	2989	2	4	7	9	11	13	16	18	20
20	3010	3032	3054	3075	3096	3118	3139	3160	3181	3201	2	4	6	8	11	13	15	17	19
21	3222	3243	3263	3284	3304	3324	3345	3365	3385	3404	2	4	6	8	10	12	14	16	18
22	3424	3444	3464	3483	3502	3522	3541	3560	3579	3598	2	4	6	8	10	12	14	15	17
23	3617	3636	3655	3674	3692	3711	3729	3747	3766	3784	2	4	6	7	9	11	13	15	17
24	3802	3820	3838	3856	3874	3892	3909	3927	3945	3962	2	4	5	7	9	11	12	14	16
25	3979	3997	4014	4031	4048	4065	4082	4099	4116	4133	2	3	5	7	9	10	12	14	15
26	4150	4166	4183	4200	4216	4232	4249	4265	4281	4298	2	3	5	7	8	10	11	13	15
27	4314	4330	4346	4362	4378	4393	4409	4425	4440	4456	2	3	5	6	8	9	11	13	14
28	4472	4487	4502	4518	4533	4548	4564	4579	4594	4609	2	3	5	6	8	9	11	12	14
29	4624	4639	4654	4669	4683	4698	4713	4728	4742	4757	1	3	4	6	7	9	10	12	13
30	4771	4786	4800	4814	4829	4843	4857	4871	4886	4900	1	3	4	6	7	9	10	11	13
31	4914	4928	4942	4955	4969	4983	4997	5011	5024	5038	1	3	4	6	7	8	10	11	12
32	5051	5065	5079	5092	5105	5119	5132	5145	5159	5172	1	3	4	5	7	8	9	11	12
33	5185	5198	5211	5224	5237	5250	5263	5276	5289	5302	1	3	4	5	6	8	9	10	12
34	5315	5328	5340	5353	5366	5378	5391	5403	5416	5428	1	3	4	5	6	8	9	10	11
35	5441	5453	5465	5478	5490	5502	5514	5527	5539	5551	1	2	4	5	6	7	9	10	11
36	5563	5575	5587	5599	5611	5623	5635	5647	5658	5670	1	2	4	5	6	7	8	10	11
37	5682	5694	5705	5717	5729	5740	5752	5763	5775	5786	1	2	3	5	6	7	8	9	10
38	5798	5809	5821	5832	5843	5855	5866	5877	5888	5899	1	2	3	5	6	7	8	9	10
39	5911	5922	5933	5944	5955	5966	5977	5988	5999	6010	1	2	3	4	5	7	8	9	10
40	6021	6031	6042	6053	6064	6075	6085	6096	6107	6117	1	2	3	4	5	6	8	9	10
41	6128	6138	6149	6160	6170	6180	6191	6201	6212	6222	1	2	3	4	5	6	7	8	9
42	6232	6243	6253	6263	6274	6284	6294	6304	6314	6325	1	2	3	4	5	6	7	8	9
43	6335	6345	6355	6365	6375	6385	6395	6405	6415	6425	1	2	3	4	5	6	7	8	9
44	6435	6444	6454	6464	6474	6484	6493	6503	6513	6522	1	2	3	4	5	6	7	8	9
45	6532	6542	6551	6561	6571	6580	6590	6599	6609	6618	1	2	3	4	5	6	7	8	9
46	6628	6637	6646	6656	6665	6675	6684	6693	6702	6712	1	2	3	4	5	6	7	7	8
47	6721	6730	6739	6749	6758	6767	6776	6785	6794	6803	1	2	3	4	5	5	6	7	8
48	6812	6821	6830	6839	6848	6857	6866	6875	6884	6893	1	2	3	4	4	5	6	7	8
49	6902	6911	6920	6928	6937	6946	6955	6964	6972	6981	1	2	3	4	4	5	6	7	8
50	6990	6998	7007	7016	7024	7033	7042	7050	7059	7067	1	2	3	3	4	5	6	7	8
51	7076	7084	7093	7101	7110	7118	7126	7135	7143	7152	1	2	3	3	4	5	6	7	8
52	7160	7168	7177	7185	7193	7202	7210	7218	7226	7235	1	2	2	3	4	5	6	7	7
53	7243	7251	7259	7267	7275	7284	7292	7300	7308	7316	1	2	2	3	4	5	6	6	7
54	7324	7332	7340	7348	7356	7364	7372	7380	7388	7396	1	2	2	3	4	5	6	6	7

LOGARITHMS (continued)

Natural Numbers	0	1	2	3	4	5	6	7	8	9	PROPORTIONAL PARTS								
											1	2	3	4	5	6	7	8	9
55	7404	7412	7419	7427	7435	7443	7451	7459	7466	7474	1	2	2	3	4	5	5	6	7
56	7482	7490	7497	7505	7513	7520	7528	7536	7543	7551	1	2	2	3	4	5	5	6	7
57	7559	7566	7574	7582	7589	7597	7604	7612	7619	7627	1	2	2	3	4	5	5	6	7
58	7634	7642	7649	7657	7664	7672	7679	7686	7694	7701	1	1	2	3	4	4	5	6	7
59	7709	7716	7723	7731	7738	7745	7752	7760	7767	7774	1	1	2	3	4	4	5	6	7
60	7782	7789	7796	7803	7810	7818	7825	7832	7839	7846	1	1	2	3	4	4	5	6	6
61	7853	7860	7868	7875	7882	7889	7896	7903	7910	7917	1	1	2	3	4	4	5	6	6
62	7924	7931	7938	7945	7952	7959	7966	7973	7980	7987	1	1	2	3	3	4	5	6	6
63	7993	8000	8007	8014	8021	8028	8035	8041	8048	8055	1	1	2	3	3	4	5	5	6
64	8062	8069	8075	8082	8089	8096	8102	8109	8116	8122	1	1	2	3	3	4	5	5	6
65	8129	8136	8142	8149	8156	8162	8169	8176	8182	8189	1	1	2	3	3	4	5	5	6
66	8195	8202	8209	8215	8222	8228	8235	8241	8248	8254	1	1	2	3	3	4	5	5	6
67	8261	8267	8274	8280	8287	8293	8299	8306	8312	8319	1	1	2	3	3	4	5	5	6
68	8325	8331	8338	8344	8351	8357	8363	8370	8376	8382	1	1	2	3	3	4	4	5	6
69	8388	8395	8401	8407	8414	8420	8426	8432	8439	8445	1	1	2	2	3	4	4	5	6
70	8451	8457	8463	8470	8476	8482	8488	8494	8500	8506	1	1	2	2	3	4	4	5	6
71	8513	8519	8525	8531	8537	8543	8549	8555	8561	8567	1	1	2	2	3	4	4	5	5
72	8573	8579	8585	8591	8597	8603	8609	8615	8621	8627	1	1	2	2	3	4	4	5	5
73	8633	8639	8645	8651	8657	8663	8669	8675	8681	8686	1	1	2	2	3	4	4	5	5
74	8692	8698	8704	8710	8716	8722	8727	8733	8739	8745	1	1	2	2	3	4	4	5	5
75	8751	8756	8762	8768	8774	8779	8785	8791	8797	8802	1	1	2	2	3	3	4	5	5
76	8808	8814	8820	8825	8831	8837	8842	8848	8854	8859	1	1	2	2	3	3	4	5	5
77	8865	8871	8876	8882	8887	8893	8899	8904	8910	8915	1	1	2	2	3	3	4	4	5
78	8921	8927	8932	8938	8943	8949	8954	8960	8965	8971	1	1	2	2	3	3	4	4	5
79	8976	8982	8987	8993	8998	9004	9009	9015	9020	9026	1	1	2	2	3	3	4	4	5
80	9031	9036	9042	9047	9053	9058	9063	9069	9074	9079	1	1	2	2	3	3	4	4	5
81	9085	9090	9096	9101	9106	9112	9117	9122	9128	9133	1	1	2	2	3	3	4	4	5
82	9138	9143	9149	9154	9159	9165	9170	9175	9180	9186	1	1	2	2	3	3	4	4	5
83	9191	9196	9201	9206	9212	9217	9222	9227	9232	9238	1	1	2	2	3	3	4	4	5
84	9243	9248	9253	9258	9263	9269	9274	9279	9284	9289	1	1	2	2	3	3	4	4	5
85	9294	9299	9304	9309	9315	9320	9325	9330	9335	9340	1	1	2	2	3	3	4	4	5
86	9345	9350	9355	9360	9365	9370	9375	9380	9385	9390	1	1	2	2	3	3	4	4	5
87	9395	9400	9405	9410	9415	9420	9425	9430	9435	9440	0	1	1	2	2	3	3	4	4
88	9445	9450	9455	9460	9465	9469	9474	9479	9484	9489	0	1	1	2	2	3	3	4	4
89	9494	9499	9504	9509	9513	9518	9523	9528	9533	9538	0	1	1	2	2	3	3	4	4
90	9542	9547	9552	9557	9562	9566	9571	9576	9581	9586	0	1	1	2	2	3	3	4	4
91	9590	9595	9600	9605	9609	9614	9619	9624	9628	9633	0	1	1	2	2	3	3	4	4
92	9638	9643	9647	9652	9657	9661	9666	9671	9675	9680	0	1	1	2	2	3	3	4	4
93	9685	9689	9694	9699	9703	9708	9713	9717	9722	9727	0	1	1	2	2	3	3	4	4
94	9731	9736	9741	9745	9750	9754	9759	9763	9768	9773	0	1	1	2	2	3	3	4	4
95	9777	9782	9786	9791	9795	9800	9805	9809	9814	9818	0	1	1	2	2	3	3	4	4
96	9823	9827	9832	9836	9841	9845	9850	9854	9859	9863	0	1	1	2	2	3	3	4	4
97	9868	9872	9877	9881	9886	9890	9894	9899	9903	9908	0	1	1	2	2	3	3	4	4
98	9912	9917	9921	9926	9930	9934	9939	9943	9948	9952	0	1	1	2	2	3	3	4	4
99	9956	9961	9965	9969	9974	9978	9983	9987	9991	9996	0	1	1	2	2	3	3	3	4

TRIGONOMETRIC FUNCTIONS

Angle θ Degrees	Angle θ Radians	cos θ	sin θ	tan θ	sec θ	csc θ	cot θ		
0° 00′	.0000	1.0000	.0000	.0000	1.000	No value	No value	1.5708	90° 00′
10	029	000	029	029	000	343.8	343.8	679	50
20	058	000	058	058	000	171.9	171.9	650	40
30	087	1.0000	087	087	000	114.6	114.6	621	30
40	116	.9999	116	116	000	85.95	85.94	592	20
50	145	999	145	145	000	68.76	68.75	563	10
1° 00′	.0175	.9998	.0175	.0175	1.000	57.30	57.29	1.5533	89° 00′
10	204	998	204	204	000	49.11	49.10	504	50
20	233	997	233	233	000	42.98	42.96	475	40
30	262	997	262	262	000	38.20	38.19	446	30
40	291	996	291	291	000	34.38	34.37	417	20
50	320	995	320	320	001	31.26	31.24	388	10
2° 00′	.0349	.9994	.0349	.0349	1.001	28.65	28.64	1.5359	88° 00′
10	378	993	378	378	001	26.45	26.43	330	50
20	407	992	407	407	001	24.56	24.54	301	40
30	436	990	436	437	001	22.93	22.90	272	30
40	465	989	465	466	001	21.49	21.47	243	20
50	495	988	494	495	001	20.23	20.21	213	10
3° 00′	.0524	.9986	.0523	.0524	1.001	19.11	19.08	1.5184	87° 00′
10	553	985	552	553	002	18.10	18.07	155	50
20	582	983	581	582	002	17.20	17.17	126	40
30	611	981	610	612	002	16.38	16.35	097	30
40	640	980	640	641	002	15.64	15.60	068	20
50	669	978	669	670	002	14.96	14.92	039	10
4° 00′	.0698	.9976	.0698	.0699	1.002	14.34	14.30	1.5010	86° 00′
10	727	974	727	729	003	13.76	13.73	981	50
20	765	971	756	758	003	13.23	13.20	952	40
30	785	969	785	787	003	12.75	12.71	923	30
40	814	967	814	816	003	12.29	12.25	893	20
50	844	964	843	846	004	11.87	11.83	864	10
5° 00′	.0873	.9962	.0872	.0875	1.004	11.47	11.43	1.4835	85° 00′
10	902	959	901	904	004	11.10	11.06	806	50
20	931	957	929	934	004	10.76	10.71	777	40
30	960	954	958	963	005	10.43	10.39	748	30
40	.0989	951	.0987	.0992	005	10.13	10.08	719	20
50	.1018	948	.1016	.1022	005	9.839	9.788	690	10
6° 00′	.1047	.9945	.1045	.1051	1.006	9.567	9.514	1.4661	84° 00′
10	076	942	074	080	006	9.309	9.255	632	50
20	105	939	103	110	006	9.065	9.010	603	40
30	134	936	132	139	006	8.834	8.777	573	30
40	164	932	161	169	007	8.614	8.556	544	20
50	193	929	190	198	007	8.405	8.345	515	10
7° 00′	.1222	.9925	.1219	.1228	1.008	8.206	8.144	1.4486	83° 00′
10	251	922	248	257	008	8.016	7.953	457	50
20	280	918	276	287	008	7.834	7.770	428	40
30	309	914	305	317	009	7.661	7.596	399	30
40	338	911	334	346	009	7.496	7.429	370	20
50	367	907	363	376	009	7.337	7.269	341	10
8° 00′	.1396	.9903	.1392	.1405	1.010	7.185	7.115	1.4312	82° 00′

		sin θ	cos θ	cot θ	csc θ	sec θ	tan θ	Radians	Degrees
								Angle θ	

TRIGONOMETRIC FUNCTIONS (continued)

Angle θ Degrees	Radians	cos θ	sin θ	tan θ	sec θ	csc θ	cot θ		
8° 00'	.1396	.9903	.1392	.1405	1.010	7.185	7.115	1.4312	82° 00'
10	425	899	421	435	010	7.040	6.968	283	50
20	454	894	449	465	011	6.900	827	254	40
30	484	890	478	495	011	765	691	224	30
40	513	886	507	524	012	636	561	195	20
50	542	881	536	554	012	512	435	166	10
9° 00'	.1571	.9877	.1564	.1584	1.012	6.392	6.314	1.4137	81° 00'
10	600	872	593	614	013	277	197	108	50
20	629	868	622	644	013	166	6.084	079	40
30	658	863	650	673	014	6.059	5.976	050	30
40	687	858	679	703	014	5.955	871	1.4021	20
50	716	853	708	733	015	855	769	1.3992	10
10° 00'	.1745	.9848	.1736	.1763	1.015	5.759	5.671	1.3963	80° 00'
10	774	843	765	793	016	665	576	934	50
20	804	838	794	823	016	575	485	904	40
30	833	833	822	853	017	487	396	875	30
40	862	827	851	883	018	403	309	846	20
50	891	822	880	914	018	320	226	817	10
11° 00'	.1920	.9816	.1908	.1944	1.019	5.241	5.145	1.3788	79° 00'
10	949	811	937	.1974	019	164	5.066	759	50
20	.1978	805	965	.2004	020	089	4.989	730	40
30	.2007	799	.1994	035	020	5.016	915	701	30
40	036	793	.2022	065	021	4.945	843	672	20
50	065	787	051	095	022	876	773	643	10
12° 00'	.2094	.9781	.2079	.2126	1.022	4.810	4.705	1.3614	78° 00'
10	123	775	108	156	023	745	638	584	50
20	153	769	136	186	024	682	574	555	40
30	182	763	164	217	024	620	511	526	30
40	211	757	193	247	025	560	449	497	20
50	240	750	221	278	026	502	390	468	10
13° 00'	.2269	.9744	.2250	.2309	1.026	4.445	4.331	1.3439	77° 00'
10	298	737	278	339	027	390	275	410	50
20	327	730	306	370	028	336	219	381	40
30	356	724	334	401	028	284	165	352	30
40	385	717	363	432	029	232	113	323	20
50	414	710	391	462	030	182	061	294	10
14° 00'	.2443	.9703	.2419	.2493	1.031	4.134	4.011	1.3265	76° 00'
10	473	696	447	524	031	086	3.962	235	50
20	502	689	476	555	032	4.039	914	206	40
30	531	681	504	586	033	3.994	867	177	30
40	560	674	532	617	034	950	821	148	20
50	589	667	560	648	034	906	776	119	10
15° 00'	.2618	.9659	.2588	.2679	1.035	3.864	3.732	1.3090	75° 00'
10	647	652	616	711	036	822	689	061	50
20	676	644	644	742	037	782	647	032	40
30	705	636	672	773	038	742	606	1.3003	30
40	734	628	700	805	039	703	566	1.2974	20
50	763	621	728	836	039	665	526	945	10
16° 00'	.2793	.9613	.2756	.2867	1.040	3.628	3.487	1.2915	74° 00'
		sin θ	cos θ	cot θ	csc θ	sec θ	tan θ	Radians	Degrees
								Angle θ	

TRIGONOMETRIC FUNCTIONS (continued)

Angle Degrees	Angle Radians	$\cos\theta$	$\sin\theta$	$\tan\theta$	$\sec\theta$	$\csc\theta$	$\cot\theta$		
16° 00′	.2793	.9613	.2756	.2867	1.040	3.628	3.487	1.2915	74° 00′
10	822	605	784	899	041	592	450	886	50
20	851	596	812	931	042	556	412	857	40
30	880	588	840	962	043	521	376	828	30
40	909	580	868	.2944	044	487	340	799	20
50	938	572	896	.3026	045	453	305	770	10
17° 00′	.2967	.9563	.2924	.3057	1.046	3.420	3.271	1.2741	73° 00′
10	.2996	555	952	089	047	388	237	712	50
20	.3025	546	.2979	121	048	357	204	683	40
30	054	537	.3007	153	048	326	172	654	30
40	083	528	035	185	049	295	140	625	20
50	113	520	062	217	050	265	108	595	10
18° 00′	.3142	.9511	.3090	.3249	1.051	3.236	3.078	1.2566	72° 00′
10	171	502	118	281	052	207	047	537	50
20	200	492	145	314	053	179	3.018	508	40
30	229	483	173	346	054	152	2.989	479	30
40	258	474	201	378	056	124	960	450	20
50	287	465	228	411	057	098	932	421	10
19° 00′	.3316	.9455	.3256	.3443	1.058	3.072	2.904	1.2392	71° 00′
10	345	446	283	476	059	046	877	363	50
20	374	436	311	508	060	3.021	850	334	40
30	403	426	338	541	061	2.996	824	305	30
40	432	417	365	574	062	971	798	275	20
50	462	407	393	607	063	947	773	246	10
20° 00′	.3491	.9397	.3420	.3640	.1064	2.924	2.747	1.2217	70° 00′
10	520	387	448	673	065	901	723	188	50
20	549	377	475	706	066	878	699	159	40
30	578	367	502	739	068	855	675	130	30
40	607	356	529	772	069	833	651	101	20
50	636	346	557	805	070	812	628	072	10
21° 00′	.3665	.9336	.3584	.3839	1.071	2.790	2.605	1.2043	69° 00′
10	694	325	611	872	072	769	583	1.2014	50
20	723	315	638	906	074	749	560	1.1985	40
30	752	304	665	939	075	729	539	956	30
40	782	293	692	.3973	076	709	517	926	20
50	811	283	719	.4006	077	689	496	897	10
22° 00′	.3840	.9272	.3746	.4040	1.079	2.669	2.475	1.1868	68° 00′
10	869	261	773	074	080	650	455	839	50
20	898	250	800	108	081	632	434	810	40
30	927	239	827	142	082	613	414	781	30
40	956	228	854	176	084	595	394	752	20
50	985	216	881	210	085	577	375	723	10
23° 00′	.4014	.9205	.3907	.4245	1.086	2.559	2.356	1.1694	67° 00′
10	043	194	934	279	088	542	337	665	50
20	072	182	961	314	089	525	318	636	40
30	102	171	.3987	348	090	508	300	606	30
40	131	159	.4014	383	092	491	282	577	20
50	160	147	041	417	093	475	264	548	10
24° 00′	.4189	.9135	.4067	.4452	1.095	2.459	2.246	1.1519	66° 00′

		$\sin\theta$	$\cos\theta$	$\cot\theta$	$\csc\theta$	$\sec\theta$	$\tan\theta$	Radians	Degrees
								Angle θ	

TRIGONOMETRIC FUNCTIONS (continued)

Angle θ Degrees	Radians	cos θ	sin θ	tan θ	sec θ	csc θ	cot θ		
24° 00′	.4189	.9135	.4067	.4452	1.095	2.459	2.246	1.1519	66° 00′
10	218	124	094	487	096	443	229	490	50
20	247	112	120	522	097	427	211	461	40
30	276	100	147	557	099	411	194	432	30
40	305	088	173	592	100	396	177	403	20
50	334	075	200	628	102	381	161	374	10
25° 00′	.4363	.9063	.4226	.4663	1.103	2.366	2.145	1.1345	65° 00′
10	392	051	253	699	105	352	128	316	50
20	422	038	279	734	106	337	112	286	40
30	451	026	305	770	108	323	097	257	30
40	480	013	331	806	109	309	081	228	20
50	509	.9001	358	841	111	295	066	199	10
26° 00′	.4538	.8988	.4384	.4877	1.113	2.281	2.050	1.1170	64° 00′
10	567	975	410	913	114	268	035	141	50
20	596	962	436	950	116	254	020	112	40
30	625	949	462	.4986	117	241	2.006	083	30
40	654	936	488	.5022	119	228	1.991	054	20
50	683	923	514	059	121	215	977	1.1025	10
27° 00′	.4712	.8910	.4540	.5095	1.122	2.203	1.963	1.0996	63° 00′
10	741	897	566	132	124	190	949	966	50
20	771	884	592	169	126	178	935	937	40
30	800	870	617	206	127	166	921	908	30
40	829	857	643	243	129	154	907	879	20
50	858	843	669	280	131	142	894	850	10
28° 00′	.4887	.8829	.4695	.5317	1.133	2.130	1.881	1.0821	62° 00′
10	916	816	720	354	134	118	868	792	50
20	945	802	746	392	136	107	855	763	40
30	.4974	788	772	430	138	096	842	734	30
40	.5003	774	797	467	140	085	829	705	20
50	032	760	823	505	142	074	816	676	10
29° 00′	.5061	.8746	.4848	.5543	1.143	2.063	1.804	1.0647	61° 00′
10	091	732	874	581	145	052	792	617	50
20	120	718	899	619	147	041	780	588	40
30	149	704	924	658	149	031	767	559	30
40	178	689	950	696	151	020	756	530	20
50	207	675	.4975	735	153	010	744	501	10
30° 00′	.5236	.8660	.5000	.5774	1.155	2.000	1.732	1.0472	60° 00′
10	265	646	025	812	157	1.990	720	443	50
20	294	631	050	851	159	980	709	414	40
30	323	616	075	890	161	970	698	385	30
40	352	601	100	930	163	961	686	356	20
50	381	587	125	.5969	165	951	675	327	10
31° 00′	.5411	.8572	.5150	.6009	1.167	1.942	1.664	1.0297	59° 00′
10	440	557	175	048	169	932	653	268	50
20	469	542	200	088	171	923	643	239	40
30	498	526	225	128	173	914	632	210	30
40	527	511	250	168	175	905	621	181	20
50	556	496	275	208	177	896	611	152	10
32° 00′	.5585	.8480	.5299	.6249	1.179	1.887	1.600	1.0123	58° 00′
		sin θ	cos θ	cot θ	csc θ	sec θ	tan θ	Radians	Degrees
								Angle θ	

TRIGONOMETRIC FUNCTIONS (continued)

Angle θ Degrees	Angle θ Radians	cos θ	sin θ	tan θ	sec θ	csc θ	cot θ		
32° 00′	.5585	.8480	.5299	.6249	1.179	1.887	1.600	1.0123	58° 00′
10	614	465	324	289	181	878	590	094	50
20	643	450	348	330	184	870	580	065	40
30	672	434	373	371	186	861	570	036	30
40	701	418	398	412	188	853	560	1.0007	20
50	730	403	422	453	190	844	550	.9977	10
33° 00′	.5760	.8387	.5446	.6494	1.192	1.836	1.540	.9948	57° 00′
10	789	371	471	536	195	828	530	919	50
20	818	355	495	577	197	820	520	890	40
30	847	339	519	619	199	812	511	861	30
40	876	323	544	661	202	804	501	832	20
50	905	307	568	703	204	796	492	803	10
34° 00′	.5934	.8290	.5592	.6745	1.206	1.788	1.483	.9774	56° 00′
10	963	274	616	787	209	781	473	745	50
20	.5992	258	640	830	211	773	464	716	40
30	.6021	241	664	873	213	766	455	687	30
40	050	225	688	916	216	758	446	657	20
50	080	208	712	.6959	218	751	437	628	10
35° 00′	.6109	.8192	.5736	.7002	1.221	1.743	1.428	.9599	55° 00′
10	138	175	760	046	223	736	419	570	50
20	167	158	783	089	226	729	411	541	40
30	196	141	807	133	228	722	402	512	30
40	225	124	831	177	231	715	393	483	20
50	254	107	854	221	233	708	385	454	10
36° 00′	.6283	.8090	.5878	.7265	1.236	1.701	1.376	.9425	54° 00′
10	312	073	901	310	239	695	368	396	50
20	341	056	925	355	241	688	360	367	40
30	370	039	948	400	244	681	351	338	30
40	400	021	972	445	247	675	343	308	20
50	429	.8004	.5995	490	249	668	335	279	10
37° 00′	.6458	.7986	.6018	.7536	1.252	1.662	1.327	.9250	53° 00′
10	487	966	041	581	255	655	319	221	50
20	516	951	065	627	258	649	311	192	40
30	545	934	088	673	260	643	303	163	30
40	574	916	111	720	263	636	295	134	20
50	603	898	134	766	266	630	288	105	10
38° 00′	.6632	.7880	.6157	.7813	1.269	1.624	1.280	.9076	52° 00′
10	661	862	180	860	272	618	272	047	50
20	690	844	202	907	275	612	265	.9018	40
30	720	826	225	.7954	278	606	257	.8988	30
40	749	808	248	.8002	281	601	250	959	20
50	778	790	271	050	284	595	242	930	10
39° 00′	.6807	.7771	.6293	.8098	1.287	1.589	1.235	.8901	51° 00′
10	836	753	316	146	290	583	228	872	50
20	865	735	338	195	293	578	220	843	40
30	894	716	361	243	296	572	213	814	30
40	923	698	383	292	299	567	206	785	20
50	952	679	406	342	302	561	199	756	10
40° 00′	.6981	.7660	.6428	.8391	1.305	1.556	1.192	.8727	50° 00′
		sin θ	cos θ	cot θ	csc θ	sec θ	tan θ	Radians	Degrees
								Angle θ	

TRIGONOMETRIC FUNCTIONS (continued)

Degrees	Radians	cos θ	sin θ	tan θ	sec θ	csc θ	cot θ		
40° 00′	.6981	.7660	.6428	.8391	1.305	1.556	1.192	.8727	50° 00′
10	.7010	642	450	441	309	550	185	698	50
20	039	623	472	491	312	545	178	668	40
30	069	604	494	541	315	540	171	639	30
40	098	585	517	591	318	535	164	610	20
50	127	566	539	642	322	529	157	581	10
41° 00′	.7156	.7547	.6561	.8693	1.325	1.524	1.150	.8552	49° 00′
10	185	528	583	744	328	519	144	523	50
20	214	509	604	796	332	514	137	494	40
30	243	490	626	847	335	509	130	465	30
40	272	470	648	899	339	504	124	436	20
50	301	451	670	.8952	342	499	117	407	10
42° 00′	.7330	.7431	.6691	.9004	1.346	1.494	1.111	.8378	48° 00′
10	359	412	713	057	349	490	104	348	50
20	389	392	734	110	353	485	098	319	40
30	418	373	756	163	356	480	091	290	30
40	447	353	777	217	360	476	085	261	20
50	476	333	799	271	364	471	079	232	10
43° 00′	.7505	.7314	.6820	.9325	1.367	1.466	1.072	.8203	47° 00′
10	534	294	841	380	371	462	066	174	50
20	563	274	862	435	375	457	060	145	40
30	592	254	884	490	379	453	054	116	30
40	621	234	905	545	382	448	048	087	20
50	650	214	926	601	386	444	042	058	10
44° 00′	.7679	.7193	.6947	.9657	1.390	1.440	1.036	.8029	46° 00′
10	709	173	967	713	394	435	030	.7999	50
20	738	153	.6988	770	398	431	024	970	40
30	767	133	.7009	827	402	427	018	941	30
40	796	112	030	884	406	423	012	912	20
50	825	092	050	.9942	410	418	006	883	10
45° 00′	.7854	.7071	.7071	1.000	1.414	1.414	1.000	.7854	45° 00′

		sin θ	cos θ	cot θ	csc θ	sec θ	tan θ	Radians	Degrees
								Angle θ	

ABBREVIATIONS FOR ENGINEERING TERMS[1]

absolute	abs
acre	spell out
acre-foot	acre-ft
air horsepower	air hp
alternating-current (as adjective)	a-c
ampere	amp
ampere-hour	amp-hr
amplitude, an elliptic function	am.
Angstrom unit	Å
antilogarithm	antilog
atmosphere	atm
atomic weight	at. wt
average	avg
avoirdupois	avdp
azimuth	az or α
barometer	bar.
barrel	bbl
Baumé	Bé
board feet (feet board measure)	fbm
boiler pressure	spell out
boiling point	bp
brake horsepower	bhp
brake horsepower-hour	bhp-hr
Brinell hardness number	Bhn
British thermal unit	Btu or B
bushel	bu
calorie	cal
candle	c
candle-hour	c-hr
candlepower	cp
cent	c or ¢
center to center	c to c
centigram	cg
centiliter	cl
centimeter	cm
centimeter-gram-second (system)	cgs
chemical	chem
chemically pure	cp
circular	cir
circular mils	cir mils
coefficient	coef
cologarithm	colog
conductivity	cond
constant	const

cord	cd
cosecant	csc
cosine	cos
cosine of the amplitude, an elliptic function	cn
cotangent	cot
coulomb	spell out
cubic	cu
cubic centimeter	cu cm, cm^3
cubic feet per minute	cfm or ft^3/min
cubic feet per second	cfs or ft^3/sec
cubic foot	cu ft or ft^3
cubic inch	cu in. or $in.^3$
cubic meter	cu m or m^3
cubic micron	cu μ or cu mu or μ^3
cubic millimeter	cu mm or mm^3
cubic yard	cu yd or yd^3
cylinder	cyl
decibel	db
degree	deg or °
degree Celsius	C
degree Fahrenheit	F
degree Kelvin	K
degree Réaumur	R
diameter	diam
direct-current (as adjective)	d-c
dollar	$
dozen	doz
dram	dr
dyne	spell out
efficiency	eff
electric	elec
electromotive force	emf
elevation	el
equation	eq
external	ext
farad	spell out or f
feet board measure (board feet)	fbm
feet per minute	ft/min or fpm
feet per second	ft/sec or fps
fluid	fl
foot	ft
foot-candle	ft-c

[1] This list of abbreviations is revised from *Abbreviations for Scientific and Engineering Terms,* approved by the American Standards Association, and published by the American Society of Mechanical Engineers, New York City.

ABBREVIATIONS FOR ENGINEERING TERMS (continued)

foot-Lambert	ft-L
foot-pound	ft-lb
foot-second (see cubic feet per second)	
freezing point	fp
fusion point	fnp
gallon	gal
gallons per minute	gal/min or gpm
gallons per second	gal/sec or gps
gram	g
gram-calorie	g-cal
haversine	hav
hectare	ha
henry	h
high-pressure (adjective)	h-p
hogshead	hhd
horsepower	hp
horsepower-hour	hp-hr
hour	hr
hundred	C
hundredweight (112 lb)	cwt
hyperbolic cosine	cosh
hyberbolic sine	sinh
hyperbolic tangent	tanh
inch	in.
inch-pound	in.-lb
inches per second	in./sec or ips
indicated horsepower	ihp
indicated horsepower-hour	ihp-hr
inside diameter	ID
internal	int
joule	j
kilocalorie	kcal
kilogram	kg
kilogram-calorie	kg-cal
kilogram-meter	kg-m
kilograms per cubic meter	kg per cu m or kg/m^3
kilograms per second	kg/sec or kgps
kiloliter	kl
kilometer	km
kilometers per second	kmps
kilovolt	kv
kilovolt-ampere	kva
kilowatt	kw
kilowatthour	kwhr

latitude	lat or ϕ
linear foot	lin ft
liter	l
logarithm (common)	log
logarithm (natural)	$\log_\varepsilon$ or ln
longitude	long. or λ
low-pressure (as adjective)	l-p
lumen	l
lumen-hour	l-hr
lumens per watt	lpw
mass	m or spell out
maximum	max
mean effective pressure	mep
melting point	mp
meter	m
meter-kilogram	m-kg
microampere	μa or mu a
microfarad	μf
microinch	μin.
micromicrofarad	$\mu\mu$f
micromicron	$\mu\mu$ or mu mu
micron	μ or mu
microvolt	μv
microwatt	μw or mu w
mile	mi or spell out
miles per hour	mi/hr or mph
miles per hour per second	mi/hr/sec or mphps
milliampere	ma
milligram	mg
millihenry	mh
millilambert	mL
milliliter	ml
millimeter	mm
millimicron	$m\mu$ or m mu
million	spell out
million gallons per day	mgd
millivolt	mv
minute	min
minute (angular measure)	'
mole	spell out
molecular weight	mol. wt
month	spell out
National Electrical Code	NEC
newton	n
ohm	spell out or Ω
ohm-centimeter	ohm-cm

ounce .... oz
ounce-foot .... oz-ft
ounce-inch .... oz-in.
outside diameter .... OD

parts per million .... ppm
peck .... pk
penny (pence) .... d
pennyweight .... dwt
pint .... pt
pound .... lb
pound-foot .... lb-ft
pound-inch .... lb-in.
pound sterling .... £
pounds per brake horsepower-hour
.... lb/bph-hr or lb per bhp-hr
pounds per cubic foot
.... lb/ft³ or lb per cu ft
pounds per square foot ..... lb/ft² or psf
pounds per square inch .... lb/in.² or psi
pounds per square inch absolute
.... lb/in. abs. or psia
power factor .... spell out or pf

quart .... qt

radian .... rad or spell out
revolutions per minute ... rev/min or rpm
revolutions per second .... rev/sec or rps
rod .... spell out
root mean square .... rms

secant .... sec
second .... sec
second (angular measure) .... ″

shaft horsepower .... shp
shilling .... s
sine .... sin
specific gravity .... sp gr
specific heat .... sp ht
square .... sq
square centimeter .... sq cm or cm²
square foot .... ft² or sq ft
square inch .... in.² or sq in.
square kilometer .... sq km or km²
square meter .... sq m or m²
square micron ...... sq μ or sq mu or μ^2
square millimeter .... sq mm or mm²
square root of mean square .... rms
standard .... std

tangent .... tan
temperature .... temp
thousand .... M
thousand pound .... kip
ton .... spell out

versed sine .... vers
volt v
volt-ampere .... va
volt-coulomb .... spell out

watt .... w
watthour .... whr
watts per candle .... wpc
week .... spell out
weight .... wt

yard .... yd
year .... yr

Appendix V

Answers to Selected Problems

10–1. *e.* 2.781
 j. 7.772
 o. 6.822
 t. 3.644
 y. 7.857
10–45. $8.51(10)^6$
10–50. $8.75(10)^1$
10–55. $3.79(10)^3$
10–60. $8.37(10)^5$
10–65. $4.35(10)^5$
10–70. $1.202(10)^6$
10–75. 1.095
10–80. $8.32(10)^3$
10–85. $6.06(10)^6$
10–90. $1.619(10)^6$
10–135. $2.53(10)^1$
10–140. $4.59(10)^{-1}$
10–145. $4.25(10)^4$
10–150. $5.91(10)^2$
10–155. $2.77(10)^{-1}$
10–160. $3.88(10)^{-3}$
10–165. $1.275(10)^8$
10–170. 1.278
10–175. $2.21(10)^3$
10–180. $5.96(10)^3$
10–225. $1.350(10)^1$
10–230. $1.524(10)^{-2}$
10–235. $9.54(10)^{-1}$
10–240. $1.099(10)^{-1}$

10–245. $2.87(10)^{-6}$
10–250. $1.437(10)^{-3}$
10–255. $2.93(10)^{-7}$
10–260. $2.96(10)^{-4}$
10–265. $5.07(10)^{-1}$
10–270. 5.64
10–355. $1.430(10)^2$
10–360. $4.46(10)^{-3}$
10–365. $2.02(10)^9$
10–370. $9.98(10)^{-1}$
10–375. 1.772
10–380. $5.27(10)^{-1}$
10–385. $3.62(10)^3$
10–390. $2.53(10)^1$
10–445. $1.079(10)^5$
10–450. $1.357(10)^6$
10–455. $8.12(10)^{-7}$
10–460. 2.08
10–465. $3.26(10)^1$
10–470. $3.68(10)^2$
10–475. $5.36(10)^2$
10–480. $1.138(10)^7$
10–560. 0.978
10–565. 0.407
10–570. 0.669
10–575. 1.397
10–580. 1.028
10–585. 0.719
10–590. 1.034

10–595. 1.856
10–600. 1.061
10–605. 88.36°
10–610. 7.25°
10–615. 0.999
10–620. 31.8°
10–625. 29.55°
10–630. 0.602
10–635. 0.235
10–640. 0.897
10–645. 1.513
10–650. 1.569
10–655. 1.168
10–660. $b = 15.97$
 $B = 23.5°$
10–665. $c = 4.09$
 $B = 15°$
10–670. $a = 599$
 $b = 1807$
10–675. $a = 677$
 $c = 678$
10–730. $1.11(10)^2$
10–735. 1.331
10–740. 0.1048
10–745. 1.0352
10–750. $6.89(10)^{11}$
10–755. 0.492
10–760. 1.433
10–765. 1.0006

10–770. 0.386

10–775. 0.8728

10–780. 0.044

10–785. 36

10–790. 3.89

10–795. 0.925

10–800. 1.018

10–805. −0.250

10–810. 3.51

10–815. −6.70

10–820. 4.495

10–825. −0.0026

10–830. $3.11(10)^1$

10–835. $2.73(10)^{-2}$

10–840. $3.97(10)^4$

10–845. $-1.230(10)^3$

10–850. $1.706(10)^5$

10–855. $8.53(10)^3$

10–860. $8.98(10)^7$

10–865. $9.41(10)^{-2}$

10–870. $5.62(10)^1$

10–875. $5.43(10)^3$

10–880. $2.75(10)^{-3}$

10–885. 1.776

10–890. $3.26(10)^3$

10–895. $2.45(10)^{12}$

10–900. $7.39(10)^4$

10–905. 1.049

10–910. $1.071(10)^{-1}$

10–915. $3.34(10)^1$

10–920. $3.24(10)^{-1}$

10–925. $1.071(10)^{-9}$

10–930. *a.* 1.039
b. 1.579
c. 3.69
d. 5.395
e. 17.61
f. 28.42
g. 74.21

10–935. *a.* $4.81 + j\,3.90$
b. $2.97 + j\,2.68$
c. $8.58 + j\,3.36$
d. $0.88 + j\,2.56$

10–940. *a.* $218\ \underline{/317.4°}$
b. $100.5\ \underline{/332.6°}$
c. $0.00803\ \underline{/320.5°}$
d. $3.65\ \underline{/327.4°}$

11–18. D = 9.57 ft

11–20. Area = 1724 ft²; wt = 6.59 (10^3) lb

11–22. V = 38.3 gal

11–24. cost = $2.24; wt = 43.6 lb

11–26. V = 525 yd³

11–28. V = 615.5 in³; wt = 301 lb

11–30. $1.170\ (10^3)$ lb

11–32. Wt = 378 lb

11–34. AB = 453 ft

11–36. $B = 74.5°; C = 29.2°;$ Area = 9.05 in²

11–38. AB = 272 ft

11–40. *(a)* = 68°F; *(b)* = 98.6°F; *(c)* = 311°F; *(d)* = 1076°F; *(e)* − 15,852°F; *(f)* = 2.20 (10^5)°F; *(g)* = 28.4°F; *(h)* = −40°F; *(i)* = −459°F

11–42. −119.2°F

11–44. Dist = 0.865 in.

11–46. Depth = 8.43 ft

11–48. P = 34.3 psig

11–50. v = 2.26 (10^2) ft²

11–52. Temp = 185°F

11–54. R = 762 lb at S 51.5° E

11–56. R = 1350 lb at S 21°45′ W

11–58. R = 425 mph at S 77° E

11–60. Brace = 1950 lb at S 6°30′ W

11–62. T_1 = 243 lb; T_2 = 172 lb

11–64. R = 231 lb at 103.5° with A

11–66. R = 124 lb at 44°15′ with A

11–68. T = 296 lb

11–70. R = 70 lb at S 75° E

11–72. R = 1788 lb at N 8°35′ W

11–74. R = 62 lb at S 35°10′ E

11–76. R = 333 lb at θ = 20.6°

11–78. R = 333 lb at N 58.6° E

11–80. R = 5.10 lb at S 39° W

11–82. R = 228 lb at S 58.7° E; R = 177 lb at S 43.8° W; comp = 128.3 lb at S 60.1° W

11–84. P = 446 lb; T = 1280 lb

11–86. M_A = 220 lb-ft

11–88. M_A = 231 lb-ft

11–90. Clockwise *(a)* 13,750 lb-ft; *(b)* 5250 lb-ft; *(c)* 1750 lb-ft; *(d)* 2250 lb-ft; *(e)* 9450 lb-ft. Counterclockwise *(a)* 26,250 lb-ft; *(b)* 14,750 lb-ft; *(c)* 9750 lb-ft; *(d)* 9500 lb-ft; *(e)* 14,300 lb-ft. M = *(a)* 12,500 lb-ft; *(b)* 9500 lb-ft; *(c)* 8000 lb-ft; *(d)* 7250 lb-ft; *(e)* 4850 lb-ft

11–92. 0 lb-ft; 395 lb-ft; 280 lb-ft; 780 lb-ft

11–94. 0 lb-ft; 2160 lb-ft; 17,600 lb-ft; 527 lb-ft

11–96. $R_R = 744$ lb; $R_L = 306$ lb

11–98. 7.37 from right end

11–100. T = 470 lb; R = 436 lb at $\theta = 14.6°$

11–102. $x = 2.58$ ft from right end

11–104. (*a*) P = 432 lb;
(*b*) $R_L = 644$ lb;
$R_R = 440$ lb

11–106. (*a*)$\theta = 19.5°$;
(*b*)T = 59.5 lb;
R = 19.8 lb

11–108. T = 1.714 (10^3) lb;
$R_A = 1.715$ (10^3) lb at 33.6°

11–110. Wt = 280 lb; N = 131.7 lb

11–112. P = 153.1 lb N = 235 lb

11–114. $AB = 1917$ lb;
$CB = 2360$ lb

11–116. $A = 3750$ lb; $R_B = 1860$ lb at 27.6°

11–118. (*a*) A = 1750 lb;
(*b*) $R_B = 1405$ lb at S 72.4° E

11–120. (*a*) $AB = 344$ lb; $R_E = 777$ lb at 26.3°; (*b*) $CG = 695$ lb; $D_x = 602$ lb; $D_y = 347$ lb

11–122. $F_x = 82.2$ lb; $F_y = 190$ lb; B = 82.2 lb

11–124. Refer to engineering handbook

11–126. 3.45 (10^{16}) electrons/sec

11–128. $R_s = 370.2$ ohm; $R_p = 40.1$ ohm

11–130. R = 6.76 (10^6) ohm

11–132. I = 0.856 amp; I = 1.198 amp

11–134. Approximately 1 megohm

11–136. Discussion

11–138. Discussion

11–140. Life = 590 hr; Life = 1665 hr

11–142. v = 4.3 (10^{-3}) volts

11–144. R = 230 ohm in series

INDEX